Table of Contents

GRAMMAR

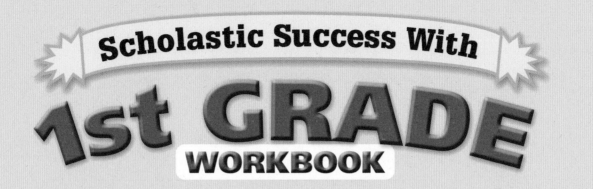

Scholastic Success With
1st GRADE
WORKBOOK

SCHOLASTIC

NEW YORK • TORONTO • LONDON • AUCKLAND • SYDNEY
MEXICO CITY • NEW DELHI • HONG KONG • BUENOS AIRES

Cover design by Anna Christian; Cover art by Rob McClurkan

Interior illustrations by Jon Buller, Reggie Holladay, Anne Kennedy, Kathy Marlin, Bob Masheris, Sherry Neidigh, Marybeth Rivera, and Carol Tiernon
Interior design by Quack & Company
Maps (pages 209–254) copyright © Linda Ward Beech

Photos ©: 257 top: KeithSzafranski/iStockphoto; 257 center: Suhaimi Sulaiman/EyeEm/Getty Images; 257 bottom: Rene Krekels/NiS/Minden Pictures/Getty Images; 257 bottom right: Derek Middleton/FLPA/Minden Pictures/Getty Images; 258: Stefan Christmann/BIA/Minden Pictures/Getty Images; 260: Dannyphoto80/Dreamstime; 263: luamduan/iStockphoto; 264 left: Napat_Polchoke/iStockphoto; 264 center: Tom Middleton/Shutterstock; 264 right: AnetteAndersen/iStockphoto; 265: NatalyaAksenova/iStockphoto; 266: yamatao/iStockphoto; 267: Top Photo Corporation/Thinkstock; 269 top: Sazonoff/iStockphoto; 269 center: photomatz/Shutterstock; 269 bottom: toomler/iStockphoto; 271: bigemrg/iStockphoto; 272: Tsekhmister/iStockphoto; 273: photomatz/Shutterstock; 274 left: IMNATURE/Thinkstock; 274 right: fotoco-istock/Thinkstock; 276 left: Pascale Gueret/Thinkstock; 276 right: McKayPhotography/Thinkstock; 280: Nanette Grebe/Shutterstock; 282: Jarenwicklund/Dreamstime; 285 top: focussucof/iStockphoto; 285 center top: Louise Wightman/iStockphoto; 285 center bottom: bamas/iStockphoto; 285 bottom: JohnPitcher/iStockphoto; 286 top: by_adr/iStockphoto; 286 left: onairjiw/iStockphoto; 286 right: Chris Knorr/Design Pics/Thinkstock; 286 bottom: Africa Studio/Shutterstock; 287: Roger Tidman/Getty Images; 290: Nati Harnik/AP Images; 293: Ariel Skelley/Getty Images; 297: Cultura RM Exclusive/Moof/Getty Images.

ISBN 978-1-338-30658-3

Scholastic Inc., 557 Broadway, New York, NY 10012
Copyright © 2018 Scholastic Inc.
All rights reserved. Printed in the U.S.A.
February 2019

2 3 4 5 6 7 8 9 10   56   24 23 22 21 20 19

WRITING

MAPS

SCIENCE

ADDITION & SUBTRACTION

MATH

"Nothing succeeds like success."

Alexandre Dumas the Elder, 1854

Dear Parent,

Congratulations on choosing this excellent educational resource for your child. Scholastic has long been a leader in educational publishing—creating quality educational materials for use in school and at home for nearly a century.

As a partner in your child's academic success, you'll want to get the most out of the learning experience offered in this book. To help your child learn at home, try following these helpful hints:

- ★ Provide a comfortable place to work.

- ★ Have frequent work sessions, but keep them short.

- ★ Praise your child's successes and encourage his or her efforts. Offer positive help when your child makes a mistake.

- ★ Display your child's work and share his or her progress with family and friends.

In this workbook you'll find hundreds of practice pages that keep kids challenged and excited as they strengthen their skills across the classroom curriculum.

The workbook is divided into eight sections: Reading Comprehension; Traditional Manuscript; Grammar; Writing; Maps; Science; Addition & Subtraction; and Math. You and your child should feel free to move through the pages in any way you wish.

The table of contents lists the activities and the skills practiced. And a complete answer key in the back will help you gauge your child's progress.

Take the lead and help your child succeed with the *Scholastic Success With 1st Grade Workbook!*

FOCUS SKILLS

The activities in this workbook reinforce age-appropriate skills and will help your child meet the following standards established as goals by leading educators.

Mathematics

★ Uses a variety of strategies when problem-solving

★ Understands and applies number concepts

★ Uses basic and advanced procedures while performing computation

★ Understands and applies concepts of measurement

★ Understands and applies concepts of geometry

Writing

★ Understands and uses the writing process

★ Uses grammatical and mechanical conventions in written compositions

Reading

★ Understands and uses the general skills and strategies of the reading process

★ Can read and understand a variety of literary texts

★ Can understand and interpret a variety of informational texts

Geography

★ Understands the characteristics and uses of maps and globes

★ Knows the location of places, geographic features, and patterns of the environment

Science

★ Plans and carries out investigations to answer questions or test solutions

★ Analyzes animals and insects, and how they interact with their environment

★ Identifies plants and their parts, and recognizes some as a food source

★ Understands the human body

★ Recognizes weather and seasonal patterns

★ Analyzes force and motion

Your Name

When you were born, your parents thought of a name for you. You might be named after someone in the family. Maybe you were named after a movie star! Almost every name has a meaning. Pamela means *honey*. Henry means *master of the house*. Ellen means *bright*. Sometimes books about baby names tell the meanings. Many of the meanings will surprise you!

Circle the name below that has the main idea of the story in it.

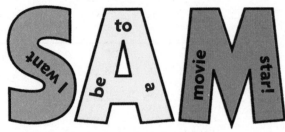

To find out the meanings of the names in the puzzle below, follow each string of beads. Copy the letters on each bead in order in the boxes.

Casey means [ ][ ][ ][ ][ ] .

George means [ ][ ][ ][ ][ ][ ][ ] .

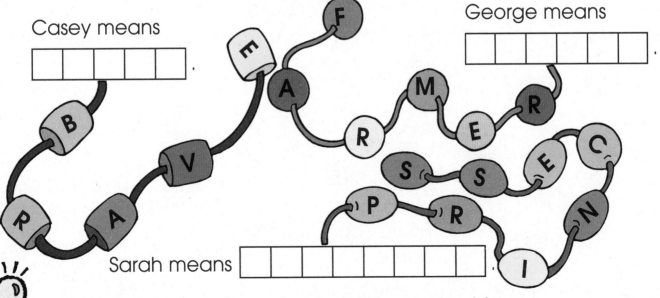

Sarah means [ ][ ][ ][ ][ ][ ][ ][ ] .

Read a book to someone at home at bedtime. Tell the main idea of the story.

Striped Critters

Details *are parts of a story. Details help you understand what the story is about.*

Skunks are small animals that live in the woods. They have black fur with one or two white stripes down their backs. Bugs are their favorite food. They also eat mice. If a skunk raises its tail, run away! Skunks can spray a very smelly liquid at anyone who bothers them.

Write the answers in the crossword puzzle.

Across:

2. What color are the stripes on a skunk's fur?

5. What is a skunk's favorite food?

Down:

1. What is another thing that skunks like to eat?

2. Where do skunks live?

3. What does a skunk raise when it is getting ready to spray?

4. What should you do if a skunk raises its tail?

💡 **Use details to describe your favorite animal.**

Ricky's Wish

Details *are parts of a story. Details help you understand what the story is about.*

Ricky loved to go camping. One day during reading class, he began to daydream about camping in the mountains. He thought about going fishing and riding horses. It would be fun to gather logs to build a campfire and cook hot dogs. He and his dad could set up the tent near some big trees. He wished he were in his canoe right now. Just then, Ricky heard his teacher say, "Ricky, it is your turn to read." Oh no! He had lost the place!

Circle these things from the story hidden in the picture below: a fish, a fishing pole, a log for the campfire, a hot dog, a tree, and a canoe.

1. Where was Ricky during this story? _____

_____

2. Where would Ricky like to have been? _____

_____

What do you like to daydream about? Write about it using details.

Going to Grammy's

Kelly is going to spend the night with her grandmother. She will need to take her pajamas, a shirt, and some shorts. Into the suitcase go her toothbrush, toothpaste, and hairbrush. Grammy told her to bring a swimsuit in case it was warm enough to swim. Mom said to pack her favorite pillow and storybooks. Dad said, "Don't forget to take Grammy's sunglasses that she left here last week." Now Kelly is ready to go!

1. Color the things that Kelly packed in her suitcase.

2. A compound word is a big word that is made up of two little words. For example, cow + boy = cowboy. Find 8 compound words in this story and circle them.

On the back of this page, make a list of things you would pack if you were going to spend the night at your grandmother's house.

George W. Bush

George W. Bush grew up in Texas. When he finished college, he worked in the oil business. Later on, he became the governor of Texas, then the 43rd president of the United States. His wife's name is Laura. They have twin daughters named Jenna and Barbara. The Bush family owns a ranch in Texas. They had two dogs named Barney and Spotty.

The Bush family also had a cat. To find out the name of their cat, write the answers in the blanks. Then copy the letters that are in the shapes into the empty shapes below.

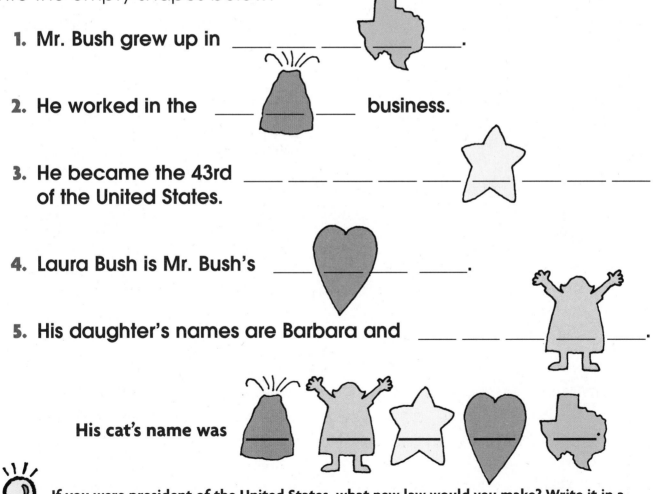

1. Mr. Bush grew up in ___ ___ ___ ___.

2. He worked in the ___ ___ ___ business.

3. He became the 43rd ___ ___ ___ ___ ___ ___ ___ ___ of the United States.

4. Laura Bush is Mr. Bush's ___ ___ ___ ___.

5. His daughter's names are Barbara and ___ ___ ___ ___ ___.

His cat's name was ___ ___ ___ ___ ___

If you were president of the United States, what new law would you make? Write it in a complete sentence, including three details.

Mr. Lee's Store

*Story events that can really happen are **real**. Story events that are make-believe are **fantasy**.*

At night, Mr. Lee locked the store and went home. That's when the fun began! The ketchup bottles stood in rows like bowling pins. Then the watermelon rolled down the aisle and knocked them down. The chicken wings flew around the room. Cans of soup stacked themselves higher and higher until they laughed so hard that they tumbled over. Carrots danced with bananas. Then it was morning. "Get back in your places!" called the milk jug. "Mr. Lee is coming!" Mr. Lee opened the door and went right to work.

Circle the cans that are make-believe.

ketchup bottles and a watermelon bowling

a talking milk jug

dancing bananas

chicken wings that can fly all by themselves

Mr. Lee went to work.

laughing soup cans

Mr. Lee went home at night.

dancing carrots

a grocery store

Draw a picture of the story on another piece of paper.

© Scholastic Inc.

Cool Clouds

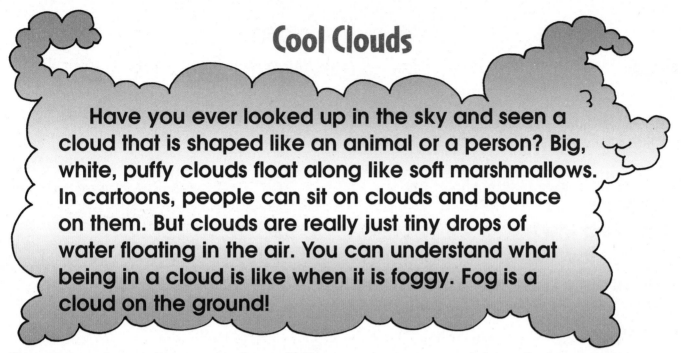

Have you ever looked up in the sky and seen a cloud that is shaped like an animal or a person? Big, white, puffy clouds float along like soft marshmallows. In cartoons, people can sit on clouds and bounce on them. But clouds are really just tiny drops of water floating in the air. You can understand what being in a cloud is like when it is foggy. Fog is a cloud on the ground!

Read each sentence below. If the sentence could really happen, color the cloud blue. If the sentence is make-believe, color it orange.

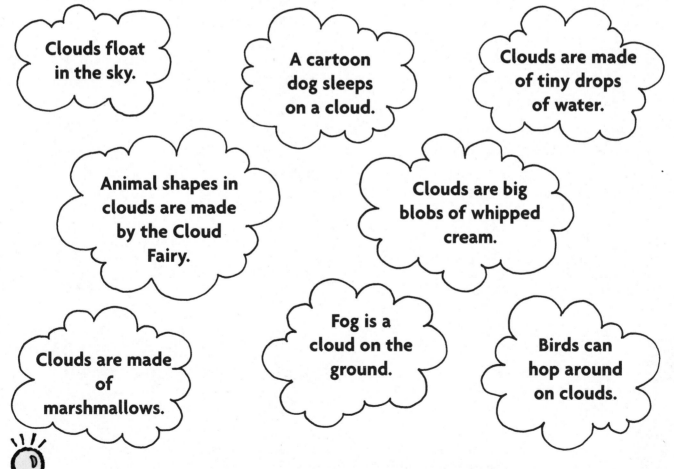

Clouds float in the sky.

A cartoon dog sleeps on a cloud.

Clouds are made of tiny drops of water.

Animal shapes in clouds are made by the Cloud Fairy.

Clouds are big blobs of whipped cream.

Clouds are made of marshmallows.

Fog is a cloud on the ground.

Birds can hop around on clouds.

Draw a picture to show a real cloud. Then draw a make-believe cloud.

Fun at the Farm

 Story events that can really happen are **real**. *Story events that are make-believe are* **fantasy**.

Read each sentence below. If it could be real, circle the picture. If it is make-believe, put an X on the picture.

 Dairy cows give milk.

 The farmer planted pizza and hamburgers.

 The pig said,"Let's go to the dance tonight!"

 The mouse ate the dinner table.

 The hay was stacked in the barn.

The chickens laid golden eggs.

 The green tractor ran out of gas.

 The newborn calf walked with wobbly legs.

The goat and the sheep got married by the big tree.

 Two crickets sang "Mary Had a Little Lamb."

 Horses sat on the couch and watched TV.

 Rain made the roads muddy.

 Four little ducks swam in the pond.

 The farmer's wife baked a pumpkin pie.

 On another sheet of paper, write one make-believe sentence about the farmer's house and one real sentence about it.

Ready for School

Sequencing *means putting the events in a story in the order they happened.*

Tara could hardly wait for school to start. Mom drove her to the store to buy school supplies. They bought pencils, crayons, scissors, and glue. When Tara got home, she wrote her name on all of her supplies. She put them in a paper sack. The next day, Tara went to school, but the principal told her and the other children to go back home. A water leak had flooded the building. Oh no! Tara would have to wait another whole week!

Number the pictures in the order that they happened in the story.

Color the supplies that Tara bought.

Swimming Lessons

Sequencing *means putting the events in a story in the order they happened.*

Last summer I learned how to swim. First, the teacher told me to hold my breath. Then I learned to put my head under water. I practiced kicking my feet. While I held on to a float, I paddled around the pool. Next, I floated to my teacher with my arms straight out. Finally, I swam using both my arms and my legs. I did it! Swimming is fun! This summer, I want to learn to dive off the diving board.

Number the pictures in the order that they happened in the story.

Unscramble the letters to tell what the person in the story wants to do next.

EALNR   **OT**   **IVDE**

_____ _____ _____ _____ _____   _____ _____   _____ _____ _____ _____

What would you like to learn to do? Draw four pictures on the back of your paper to show how to do it.

Fun at the Beach

Jack and Joni went to the beach today. Mom spread a blanket on the sand, and they had a picnic. It got very hot, so Jack and Joni jumped into the cold water. They climbed onto a big yellow raft. The waves made the raft go up and down. Later, they played in the sand and built sandcastles. Jack and Joni picked up pretty shells. Joni found a starfish. What a fun day!

1. Color the pictures below that are from the story. Put an X on the ones that don't belong.

2. In the third sentence, find two words that are opposites of each other and circle them with a red crayon.

3. In the fifth sentence, find two more words that are opposites of each other and circle them with a blue crayon.

4. Draw a box around the compound word that tells what Joni found.

5. What color was the raft? Show your answer by coloring the picture at the top of the page.

Write three sentences that tell how to get ready to play your favorite sport.

My New Rug

When you use your own thoughts to answer the question, "How could that have happened?", you are **drawing conclusions**.

I bought a fancy rug today. It was made of brightly-colored yarn. I placed it on the floor in front of the TV and sat on it. All of a sudden, it lifted me up in the air! The rug and I flew around the house. Then out the door we went. High above the trees, we soared like an eagle. Finally, it took me home, and we landed in my backyard.

How could that have happened? To find out, use your crayons to trace over each line. Use a different color on each line. Write the letter from that line in the box at the bottom of the rug.

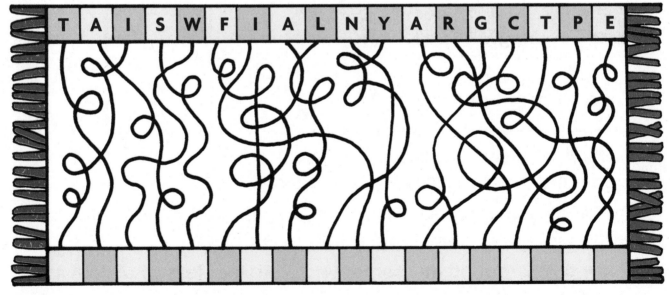

| T | A | I | S | W | F | I | A | L | N | Y | A | R | G | C | T | P | E |

Could this story really happen? Draw a rug around your answer.

Yes   **No**

You left your ball on the steps. Your mother came down the steps carrying the laundry basket. Draw a picture of what you think happened.

Polly Want a Cracker?

Have you ever heard a parrot talk? Parrots are able to copy sounds that they hear. You can train a parrot to repeat words, songs, and whistles. But a parrot cannot say words that it has never heard. People can use words to make new sentences, but most parrots cannot.

Read each sentence. If it is true, color the parrot under True.
If it is false, color the parrot under False.

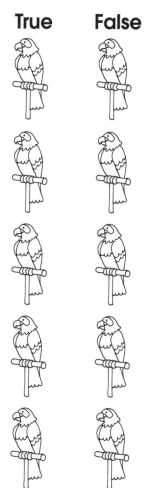

True   **False**

1. You could teach a parrot to sing "Happy Birthday."

2. You could ask a parrot any question, and it could give the answer.

3. A parrot could make up a fairy tale.

4. If a parrot heard your mom say, "Brush your teeth," every night, he could learn to say it, too.

5. It is possible for a parrot to repeat words in Spanish.

Write what would happen if a parrot heard you say, "No, I can't" too often.

You Be the Artist

Picturing a story can help the reader understand it better.

An artist drew the pictures that are in this book. Now it is your turn to be the artist! Read each sentence very carefully. Draw exactly what you read about in the sentence.

1. **The green and yellow striped snake wiggled past the ants.**

2. **Wildflowers grew along the banks of the winding river.**

3. **On her sixth birthday, Shannon had a pink birthday cake shaped like a butterfly.**

Now write your own sentence and illustrate it.

A Stormy Day

Big, black clouds appeared in the sky. Lightning struck the tallest tree. The scared cow cried, "Moo!" It rained hard. Soon there was a mud puddle by the barn door. Hay blew out of the barn window.

Read the story above. Then go back and read each sentence again. Add to the picture everything that the sentences describe.

Who Am I?

 Use details from the story to make decisions about the characters.

Circle the picture that answers the riddle.

1. I have feathers. I also have wings, but I don't fly. I love to swim in icy water. Who am I?

2. I am 3 weeks old. I drink milk. I cry when my diaper is wet. Who am I?

3. I live in the ocean. I swim around slowly, looking for something to eat. I have six more arms than you have. Who am I?

4. I am an insect. If you touch me, I might bite you! I make tunnels under the ground. I love to come to your picnic! Who am I?

5. I am a female. I like to watch movies and listen to music. My grandchildren love my oatmeal cookies. Who am I?

6. I am a large mammal. I live in the woods. I have fur. I stand up and growl when I am angry. Who am I?

7. I wear a uniform. My job is to help people. I ride on a big red truck. Who am I?

 Write your own riddle and let the class guess the answer.

What's Going On?

Use story details to help you make decisions about the story.

James was the first boy in Miss Lane's class to sneeze. He sneezed and sneezed until his mom came to take him home. The next day, Amy and Jana started sneezing. The next Monday, six more children were absent. Finally, everyone got well and came back to school. But, this time Miss Lane was absent. Guess what was wrong with her!

Circle the correct answers.

1. **What do you think was wrong with the children?**

head cold   head lice   broken arms

2. **How do you know?**

The children sneezed.

The children came back to school.

3. **How many children in all got sick?**

4. **Why do you think Miss Lane was absent? Write your answer.**

_____

_____

Make a Cartoon

Read the sentence below each picture. In the bubbles, write what each character could be saying.

Mr. Giraffe asked Mr. Zebra why he had stripes. Mr. Zebra didn't know.

Mr. Giraffe said that he should ask Mrs. Owl. Mr. Zebra agreed.

Mr. Zebra asked Mrs. Owl why he had stripes. Mrs. Owl laughed.

Mrs. Owl told Mr. Zebra that the Magic Fairy painted him that way!

 If Mr. Giraffe asked Mrs. Owl why he had such a long neck, what do you think she would say?

Clean Your Room

 Grouping like things together makes it easier to remember what you read.

Mom says, "Let's go out for ice cream! Clean your room, and then we will go." Your room is a mess. You need to put the blocks in the basket. The crayons must go in their box. The books must go on the shelf, and the marbles go in the jar. You can do it. Just think about that hot fudge sundae!

Draw a line from each item on the floor to the place it belongs. Color what you could use in school red. Color what are toys blue.

Circle the food that does not belong in an ice cream store.

 Fold a sheet of paper in half. Write "hot" on one side and "cold" on the other side. Draw four foods on each side of the paper that go with the heading.

Going to the Mall

Look for similarities when grouping items.

Read the words in the Word Box. Write each word in the place where you would find these things at the mall.

Word Box

tickets	sandals	high heels	beans	big screen
tulip bulbs	peppers	fertilizer	popcorn	gardening gloves
sneakers	burritos	boots	pots	candy	tacos

Sandie's Shoe Store

Movie Town Cinema

PEPE'S MEXICAN FOOD

Gale's Gardening Goodies

On another sheet of paper, draw the following items in a toy store or a clothing store: jump rope, blue jeans, basketball, doll, sweatshirt, stocking cap, wooden train, pajamas.

My Favorites

This page is all about you! Read the categories and write your own answers.

My Favorite TV Shows	My Favorite Foods	My Favorite Sports
_____	_____	_____
_____	_____	_____
_____	_____	_____

Draw two of your favorite people here and write their names.

Favorite Color

_____

Favorite Holiday

_____

Favorite Song

_____

Favorite Movie

_____

Favorite School Subject

_____

Favorite Thing to Do After School

_____

Favorite Thing to Do With My Family

_____

Trade pages with friends and read what they wrote. You might get to know them a little better!

Ouch!

Use story details to make a guess of what will happen next.

Mia and Rosa were playing hospital. Mia was the patient, and Rosa was the doctor. Rosa pretended to take Mia's temperature. "You have a fever," she said. "You will have to lie down." Mia climbed onto the top bunk bed. "You need to sleep," Dr. Rosa said. Mia rolled over too far and fell off the top bunk. "O-o-o-h, my arm!" yelled Mia. Her mother came to look. It was broken!

What do you think happened next? Write your answer here.

_____

To find out if your answer is correct, finish the sentence below by coloring only the spaces that have a dot in them.

Mia had to go to

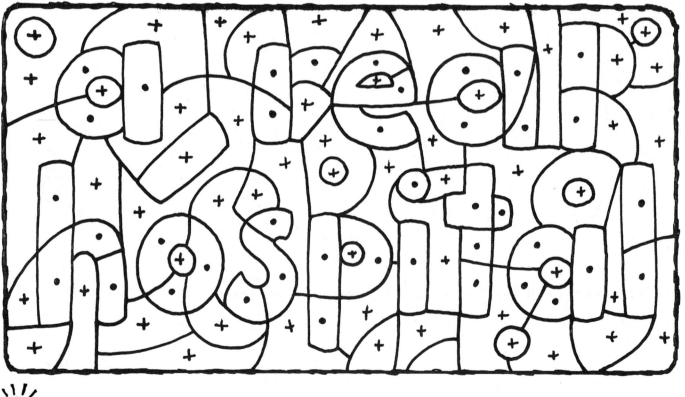

If Mia hadn't fallen off the bed, how do you think this story would have ended? Draw your answer.

What Will Sam Do?

One day, Sam was riding his bike to the baseball game. He had to be on time. He was the pitcher. Just ahead, Sam saw a little boy who had fallen off his bike. His knee was bleeding, and he was crying. Sam asked him if he was okay, but the boy couldn't speak. Sam knew the boy needed help getting home. If he stopped to help, he might be late for the game. Sam thought about it. He knew he had to do the right thing.

What do you think Sam did next? There are two paths through the maze. Draw a line down the path that shows what you think Sam did next.

What sentence from the story gives you a hint about what Sam decided to do? Write that sentence below.

_____

 The maze shows two ways the story could end. Draw a different ending to the story and tell about your picture.

Riddle Fun

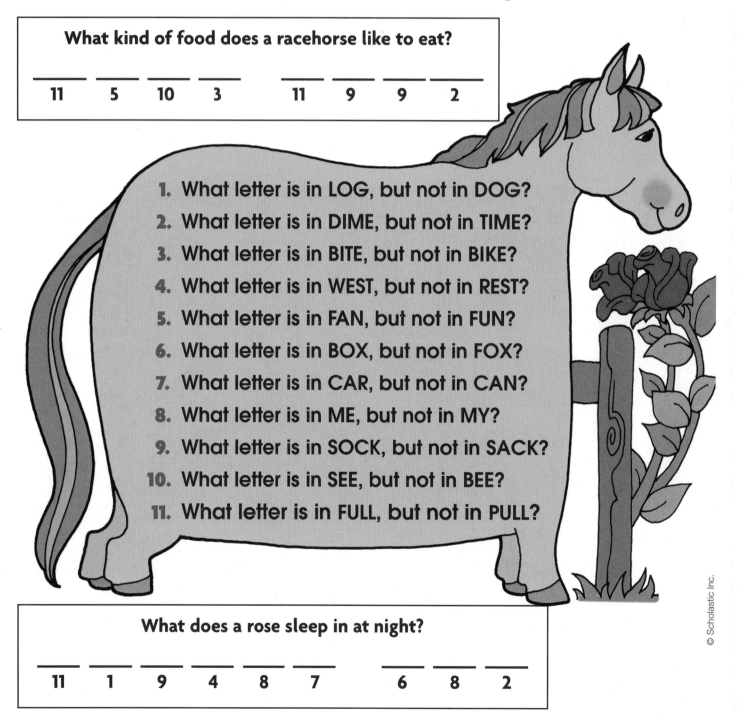

Compare *means to look for things that are the same.*
Contrast *means to look for things that are different.*

To solve the riddles in each box, read the clues in the horse.
Then write the letters in the blanks with the matching numbers.

What kind of food does a racehorse like to eat?

__ __ __ __ __ __ __ __
11 5 10 3   11 9 9 2

1. What letter is in LOG, but not in DOG?
2. What letter is in DIME, but not in TIME?
3. What letter is in BITE, but not in BIKE?
4. What letter is in WEST, but not in REST?
5. What letter is in FAN, but not in FUN?
6. What letter is in BOX, but not in FOX?
7. What letter is in CAR, but not in CAN?
8. What letter is in ME, but not in MY?
9. What letter is in SOCK, but not in SACK?
10. What letter is in SEE, but not in BEE?
11. What letter is in FULL, but not in PULL?

What does a rose sleep in at night?

__ __ __ __ __ __   __ __ __
11 1 9 4 8 7   6 8 2

Twins

Holly and Polly are twins. They are in the first grade. They look just alike, but they are very different. Holly likes to play softball and soccer. She likes to wear her hair braided when she goes out to play. She wears sporty clothes. Recess is her favorite part of school. Polly likes to read books and paint pictures. Every day she wears a ribbon in her hair to match her dress. Her favorite thing about school is going to the library. She wants to be a teacher some day.

Look at the pictures of Holly and Polly. Their faces look alike. Circle the things in both pictures that are different from each other.

Draw two lines under the words that tell what Holly and Polly do that is the same.

They play sports.   They love to paint.   They are in the first grade.

 Write rhyming names for twins that are boys. What is alike about them? What is different?

Soldier Dads

Juan's dad and Ann's dad are soldiers. Juan's dad is a captain in the Navy. He sails on the ocean in a large ship. Ann's dad is a pilot in the Air Force. He flies a jet. Juan and Ann miss their dads when they are gone for a long time. They write them letters and send them pictures. It is a happy day when their dads come home!

Draw a ☺ in the column under the correct dad.
Some sentences may describe both dads.

	Juan's dad	Ann's dad	Both dads
1. He is a captain.			
2. He works on a ship.			
3. Sometimes he is gone for a long time.			
4. He is a pilot.			
5. His child writes to him.			
6. He is in the Air Force.			
7. He is in the Navy.			
8. It is a happy time when he comes home.			
9. He flies a jet.			
10. He is a soldier.			

Dinosaur Clues

How do we know that dinosaurs were real? It is because their bones have been found in rocks. Sometimes scientists have found dinosaur footprints where mud later turned to stone. These kinds of rocks are called fossils. Fossils give us clues about how big the dinosaurs were. Some were small and some were very large. Scientists say a diplodocus was as big as three school buses!

1. Color the picture that shows scientists working.

2. Color the picture of a fossil.

3. Color the picture of a diplodocus.

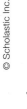

Find and write the names of three more dinosaurs.

Amazing Animal Facts

Read each sentence. Then color the picture that tells the meaning of the underlined word.

1. Sea lions sometimes sleep in the water with one <u>flipper</u> up in the air.

an arm like a paddle   a beak   a feather

2. Even though whale sharks are the biggest fish in the world, they are <u>harmless</u> to people.

reddish brown   not dangerous   very tiny

3. Horses use their tails to <u>swat</u> pesky flies.

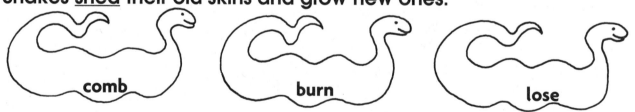

slap at   catch   eat

4. Snakes <u>shed</u> their old skins and grow new ones.

comb   burn   lose

5. Squirrels <u>bury</u> acorns and nuts to eat when winter comes.

bake   hide in the ground   steal

Write an interesting fact about two other animals.

A Tiny Town

Have you ever seen a prairie dog <u>town</u>? That's where <u>prairie dogs</u> live, but there are no buildings or houses. They live underground. They dig deep into the dirt making <u>burrows</u>. Along the burrows, here and there, are <u>chambers</u> for sleeping or storing food. One chamber is lined with grass for the babies. Sometimes prairie dogs have <u>unwanted</u> <u>guests</u> in their town, like rattlesnakes!

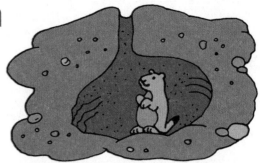

Use the code below to learn what some of the words in the story mean. Copy the matching letters in the blanks.

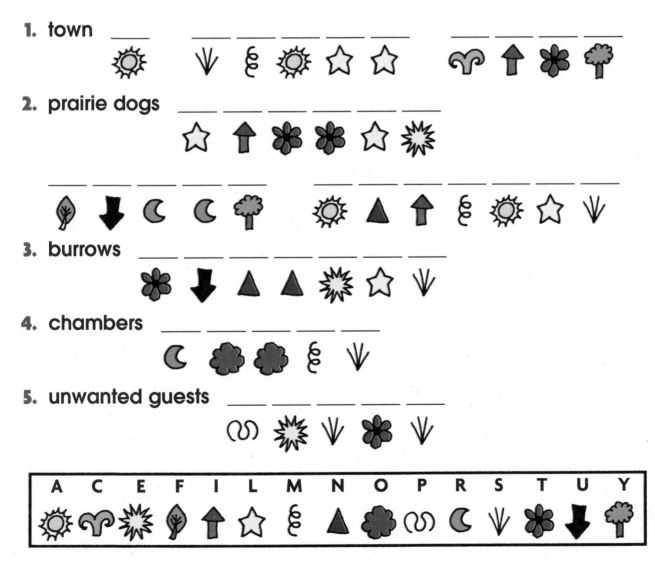

Oops!

*In a story, there is usually a reason something happens. This is the **cause**. What happens as a result is the **effect**.*

Sandy went on a vacation in the mountains with her parents and little brother Austin. They were staying in a small cabin without any electricity or running water. It was fun to have lanterns at night and to bathe in the cold mountain stream. The biggest problem for Sandy was she missed her best friend, Kendra. Sandy found her dad's cell phone and called Kendra. They talked for nearly an hour! When Sandy's dad went to call his office, the cell phone was dead. He was NOT a happy camper!

Draw a line to match the first part of each sentence to the second part that makes it true.

1. Sandy used lanterns at night because

2. Sandy and Austin bathed in a stream because

3. Sandy felt better about missing Kendra because

4. Sandy's dad could not call his office because

she talked to her on the cell phone.

the cabin had no running water.

the cabin had no electricity.

the cell phone was dead.

Write about something you did that caused a huge "effect."

Wanda Wiggleworm

 *In a story, there is usually a reason something happens.
This is the **cause**. What happens as a result is the **effect**.*

Wanda Wiggleworm was tired of
living alone in the flowerpot, so she
decided to live it up. Last night, Wanda
went to the Ugly Bug Ball. She looked her
best, all slick and slimy. Carl Caterpillar
asked her to dance. They twisted and
wiggled around and around to the
music. All of a sudden, they got tangled up. They tried to get free,
but instead, they tied themselves in a knot! What would they do?
They decided to get married, and they lived happily ever after.

Unscramble each sentence about the story.
Write the new sentence on the line.

tangled	worms	when	got	danced.	they	The	up

_____

_____

in	knot	They	married.	a	they	were	so	got	tied

_____

_____

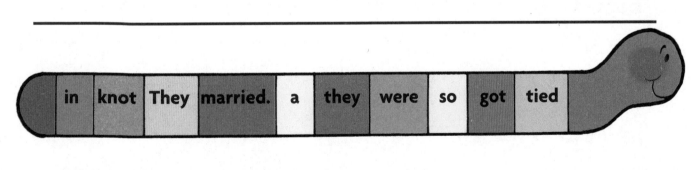

**Tim fell asleep on his raft while playing in the lake. Draw a picture of what you think the
effect was on Tim.**

School Rules

It is important to follow the rules at school. Read each rule below. Find the picture that shows what would happen if students DID NOT follow that rule. Write the letter of the picture in the correct box.

1. You must walk, not run, in the halls. ☐

2. Do not chew gum at school. ☐

3. Come to school on time. ☐

4. When the fire alarm rings, follow the leader outside. ☐

5. Listen when the teacher is talking. ☐

6. Keep your desk clean. ☐

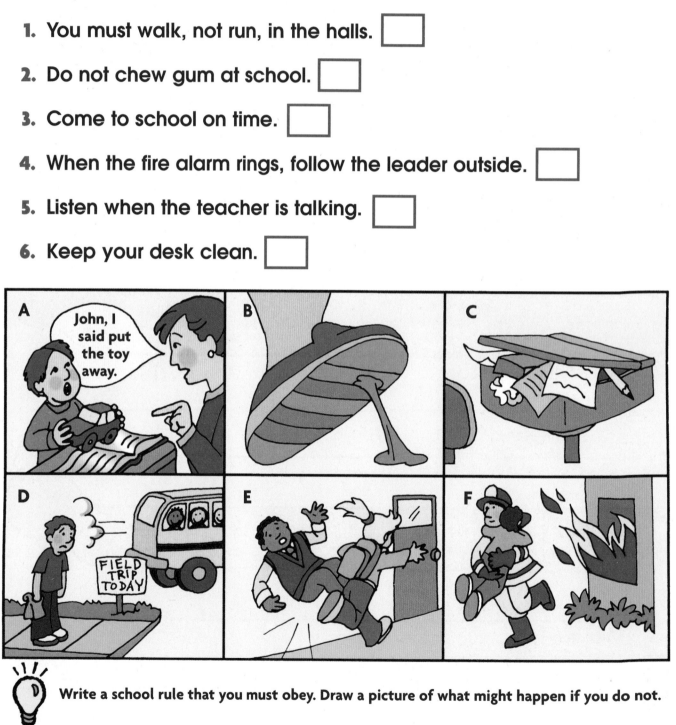

💡 **Write a school rule that you must obey. Draw a picture of what might happen if you do not.**

© Scholastic Inc.

Mixed-Up Margie

A character is a person or animal in a story. To help readers understand a character better, a story often gives details about the character.

Once upon a time there was a mixed-up queen named Margie. She got things mixed up. She wore her crown on her arm. She wore a shoe on her head. She painted every fingernail a different color. Then she painted her nose red! She used a fork to hold her hair in place. She wore a purple belt around her knees. The king didn't mind. He always wore his clothes backward!

Use the story and your crayons to help you follow these instructions:

1. Draw Margie's crown.
2. Draw her shoe.
3. Paint her fingernails and nose.
4. Draw what goes in her hair.
5. Draw her belt.

Circle the correct answer:

6. **What makes you think Margie is mixed up?**

    the way she dresses

    the way she talks

7. **What makes you think the king is mixed up, too?**

    He talks backward.

    He wears his clothes backward.

Pretend tomorrow is Mixed-Up Day. Describe what you will wear as a mixed-up character.

Miss Ticklefoot

I love Miss Ticklefoot. She is my first-grade teacher.

To find out more about her, read each sentence below. Write a word in each blank that tells how she feels. The Word Box will help you.

Word Box

| sad | scared | silly | worried | happy | surprised |

1. **Miss Ticklefoot smiles when we know the answers.**

   _____

2. **She is concerned when one of us is sick.**

   _____

3. **She makes funny faces at us during recess.**

   _____

4. **She cried when our fish died.**

   _____

5. **She jumps when the fire alarm rings.**

   _____

6. **Her mouth dropped open when we gave her a present!**

   _____

© Scholastic Inc.

Different Friends

When Ty was four years old, he had two make-believe friends named Mr. Go-Go and Mr. Sasso. They lived in Ty's closet. When there was no one else around, Ty talked to Mr. Go-Go while he played with his toys. Mr. Go-Go was a good friend. He helped put Ty's toys away. Mr. Sasso was not a good friend. Some days he forgot to make Ty's bed or brush Ty's teeth. One day he even talked back to Ty's mother. Another day Dad said, "Oh my! Who wrote on the wall?" Ty knew who did it . . . Mr. Sasso!

Read the phrase inside each crayon. If it describes Mr. Go-Go, color it green. If it describes Mr. Sasso, color it red. If it describes both, color it yellow.

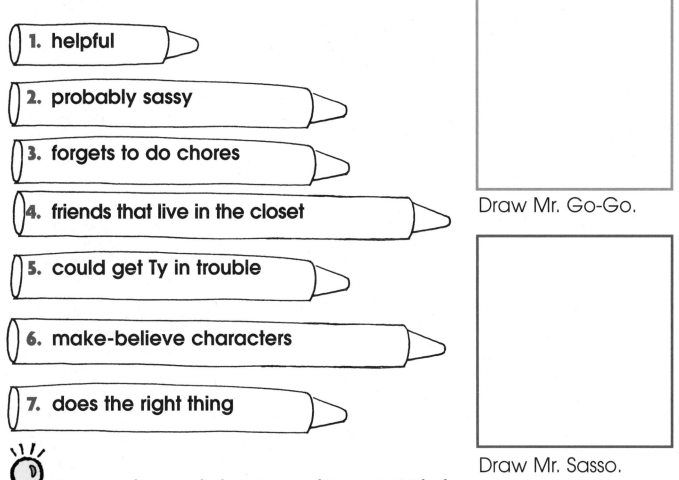

1. helpful

2. probably sassy

3. forgets to do chores

4. friends that live in the closet

5. could get Ty in trouble

6. make-believe characters

7. does the right thing

Draw Mr. Go-Go.

Draw Mr. Sasso.

Write something you think Mr. Sasso and Mr. Go-Go might do.

Poetry

A poem paints a picture with words. It often uses rhyming words.

Colorful Sky
When thunderstorms are near
Colored strips appear.
At the end, I'm told
There'll be a pot of gold.

Draw what it is.

1. Draw a red line under the word that rhymes with <u>near</u>.

2. Draw a green line under the word that rhymes with <u>told</u>.

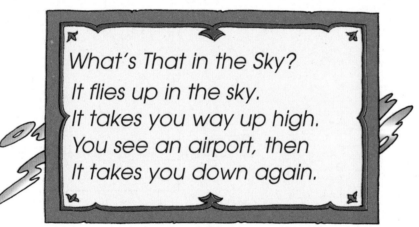

What's That in the Sky?

It flies up in the sky.
It takes you way up high.
You see an airport, then
It takes you down again.

Draw what it is.

3. Draw a blue circle around the word that rhymes with <u>sky</u>.

4. Draw a brown circle around the word that rhymes with <u>then</u>.

5. Finish this two-line poem:

    I wish that I could see

    A giant bumble_____.

Draw what it is.

Now see if you can make up your own two-line poem using these rhyming words at the end of each line: GO and SNOW.

A Fable

A fable is a story that teaches a lesson. This fable was written many, many years ago.

The Dog and His Shadow

A dog carried a piece of meat in his mouth. He crossed over a river on a low bridge. He looked down into the water and saw his reflection. It looked like another dog with a piece of meat larger than his. The dog snapped at the other dog's meat. When he did, his own meat dropped into the water. Now the dog didn't have any meat at all.

Draw a box around the lesson that the story teaches:

1. **Two dogs are better than one.**

2. **Don't be greedy. Be happy with what you have.**

Color only the pictures of things that you read about in the story:

Write a complete sentence telling what the dog should have done.

Library Books

A library has many different kinds of books.

It is fun to check books out of the library. Have you ever read *The Rainbow Fish* by Marcus Pfister? It is a story about a very special fish. His scales were blue, green, and purple. He also had some shiny, silver scales. The other fish wanted him to share his shiny scales with them, but he said no. No one would be his friend. Later, he decided to give each fish one of his shiny scales. It was better to lose some of his beauty and have friends than to keep them to himself.

Connect the dots. You will see something from the book.

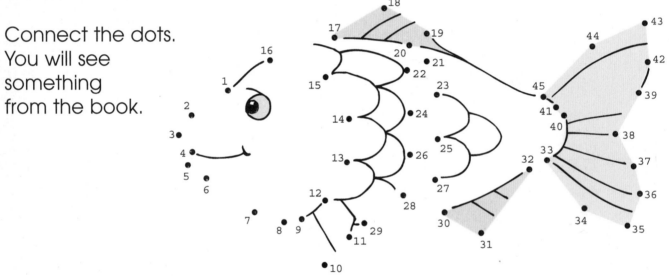

1. Draw a blue circle around the word that tells what this book is about:

running   lying   sharing   eating

2. Copy the name of the author here.

_____

_____

If you grew up to be an author, what would you write about? Make a pretty book cover that includes the title of your book.

© Scholastic Inc.

Scholastic Success With

TRADITIONAL MANUSCRIPT

Aa

Trace and write.

A A A

a a a

A a

Adam Ape is active.

Annie asked Alice.

Bb

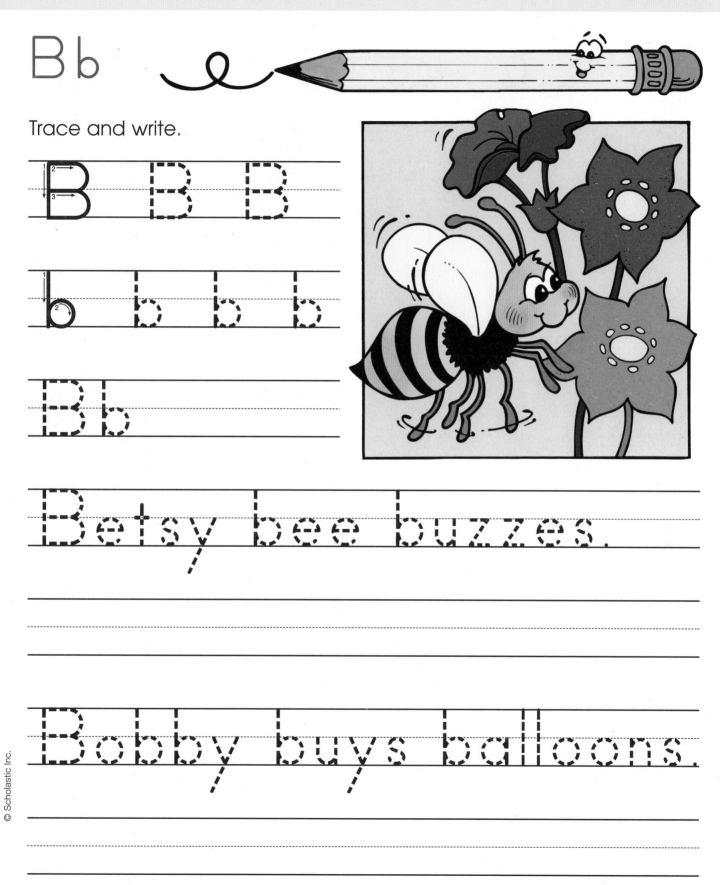

Trace and write.

B B B B

b b b b

Bb

Betsy bee buzzes.

Bobby buys balloons.

Cc

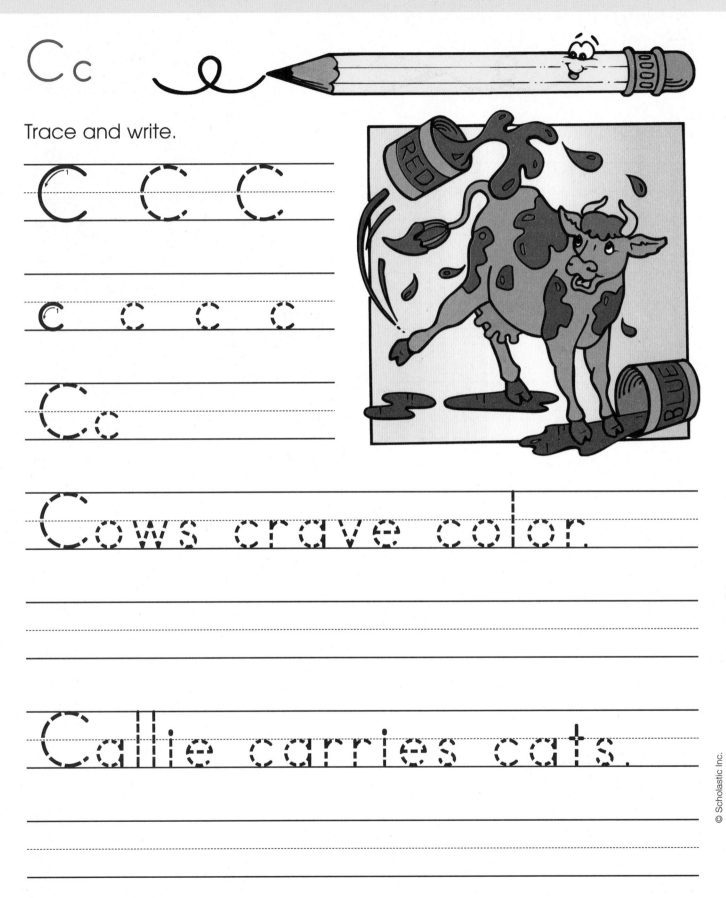

Trace and write.

C C C C

c c c c c

Cc

Cows crave color.

Callie carries cats.

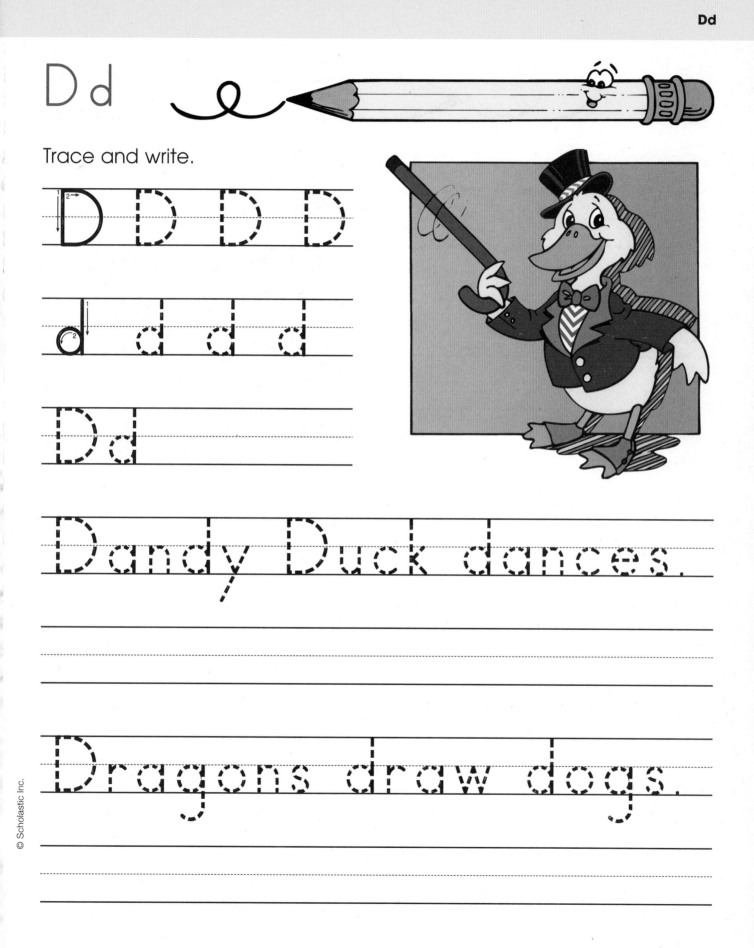

Dd

Trace and write.

D D D D D

d d d d

Dd

Dandy Duck dances.

Dragons draw dogs.

Ee

Trace and write.

E E E E E

e e e e

E e

Ellie Emu is elegant.

Ed eats eight eggs.

F f

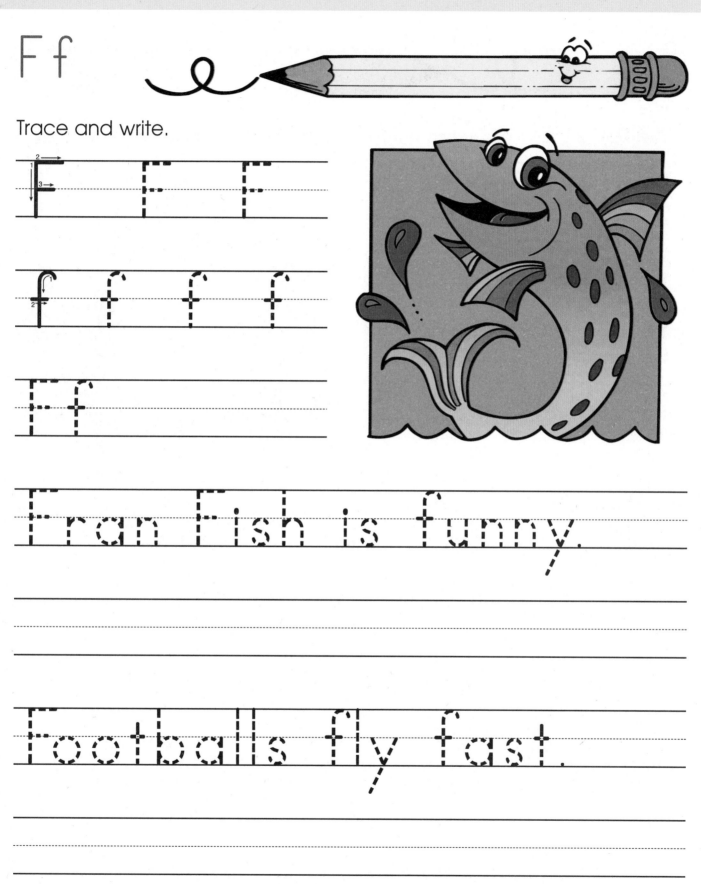

Trace and write.

F F F

f f f

F f

Fran Fish is funny.

Footballs fly fast.

G g

Trace and write.

G   G   G

g   g   g

Gg

Gus Goose giggles.

Greta grows greens.

Hh

Trace and write.

H H H H

h h h h

Hh

Hal Hippo is happy.

Hannah hangs hats.

Ii

Trace and write.

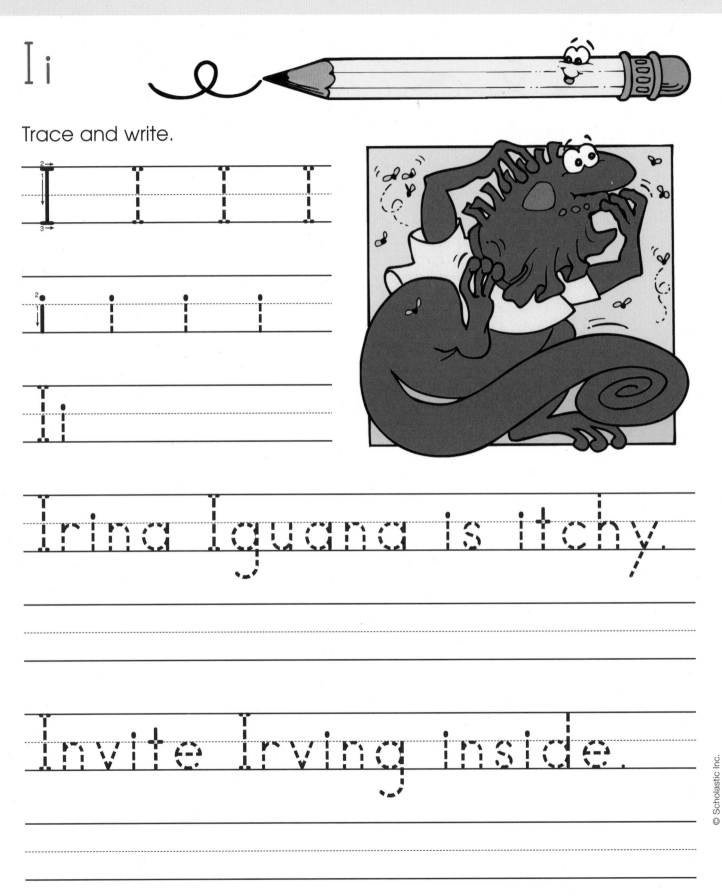

I I I I

i i i i i

Ii

Irina Iguana is itchy.

Invite Irving inside.

Jj

Trace and write.

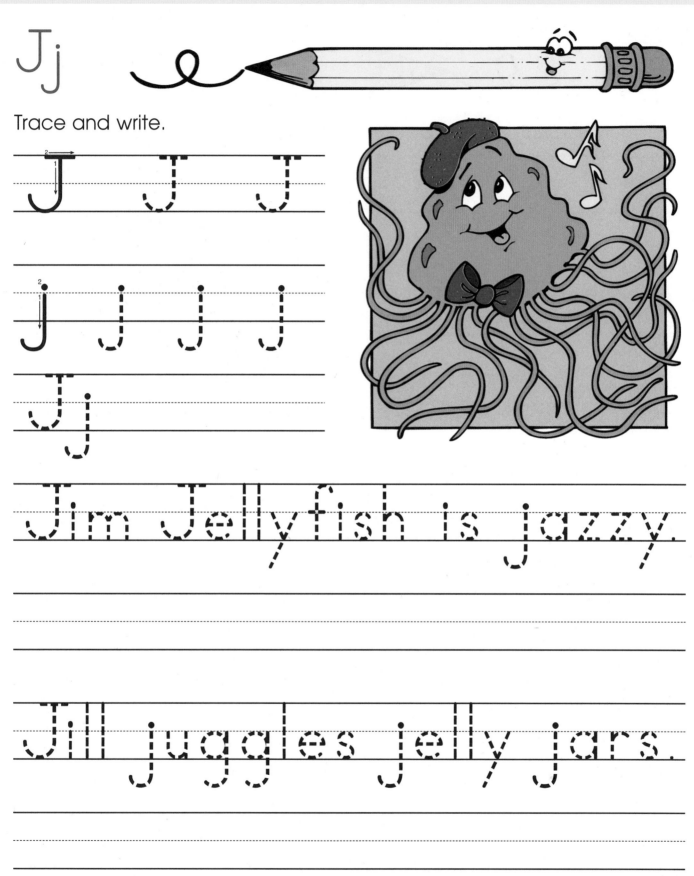

J J J

j j j j

Jj

Jim Jellyfish is jazzy.

Jill juggles jelly jars.

Kk

Trace and write.

K K K K K

k k k k k

Kk

Kyle Kangaroo kicks.

Katie keeps kittens.

LI

Trace and write.

Lyle Lion looks lost.

Lindy loves lollipops.

Mm

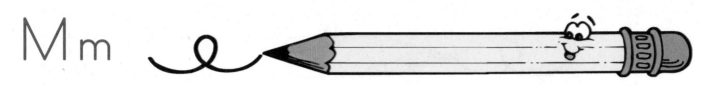

Trace and write.

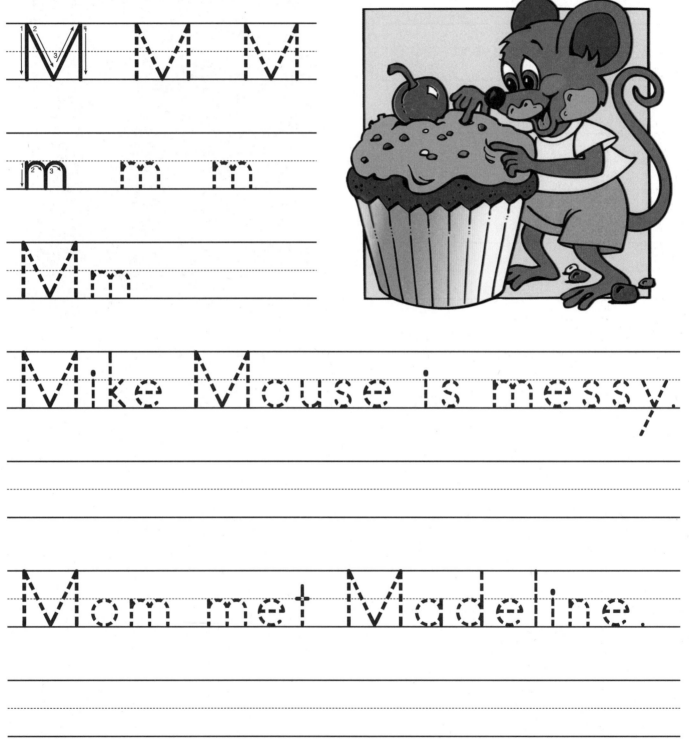

M M M

m m m

Mm

Mike Mouse is messy.

Mom met Madeline.

Nn

Trace and write.

N N N N

n n n n

Nn

Nikki Newt needs naps.

Nurse Ned nibbles.

Trace and write.

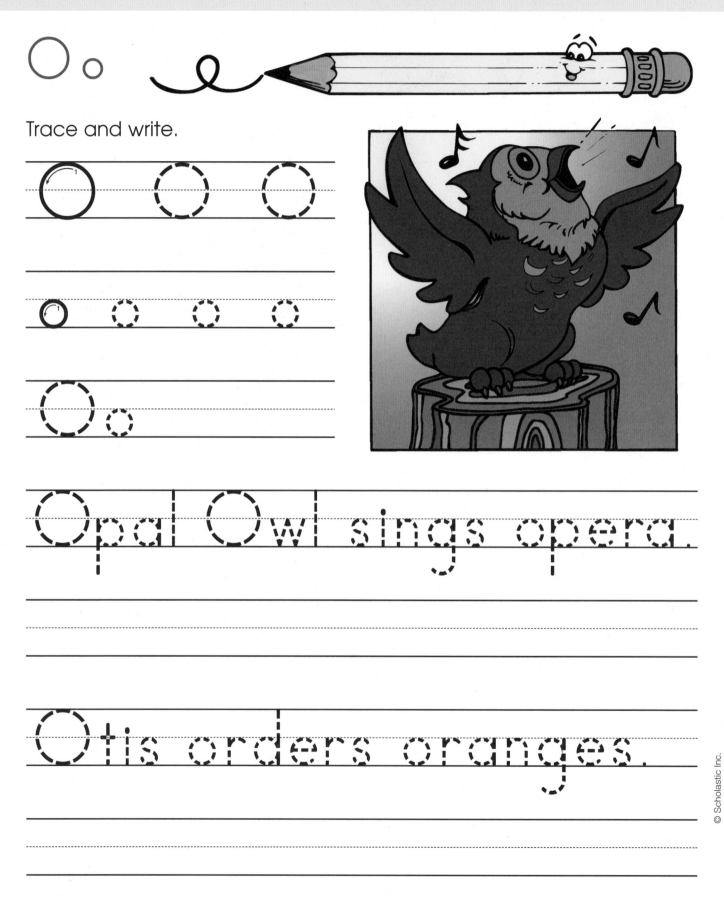

Opal Owl sings opera.

Otis orders oranges.

P p

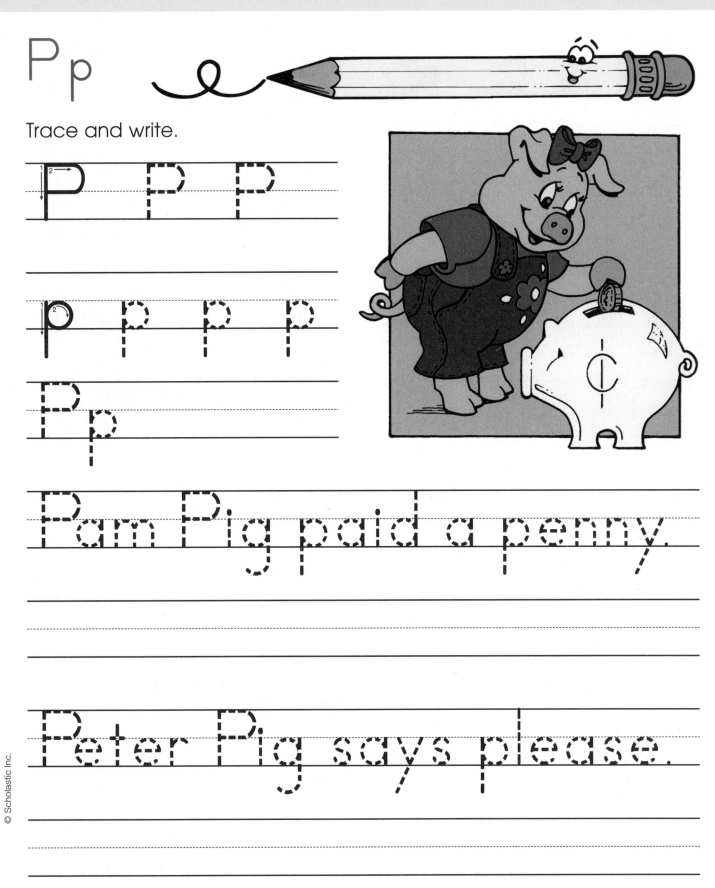

Trace and write.

P   P   P

p   p   p   p

P p

Pam Pig paid a penny.

Peter Pig says please.

Q q

Trace and write.

Q

q

Q q

Quinn Quail is quiet.

Quebec is quite nice.

shhhh!

Rr

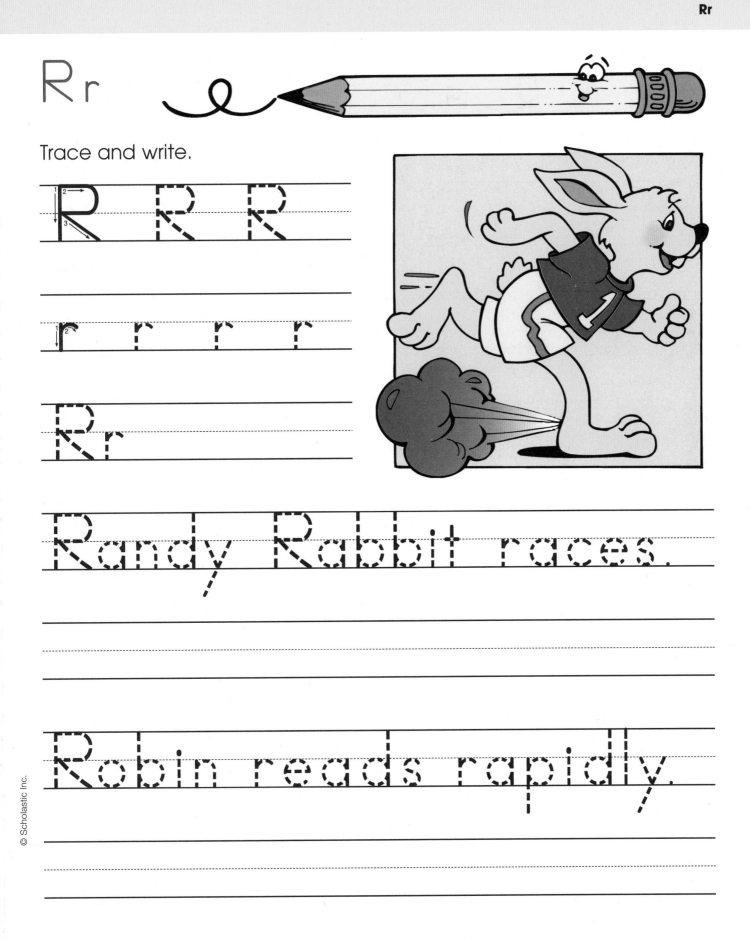

Trace and write.

R R R R

r r r r

Rr

Randy Rabbit races.

Robin reads rapidly.

S s

Trace and write.

S S S S S

s s s s s

Ss

Susanna Seal stars.

Sam sees sailboats.

Tt

Trace and write.

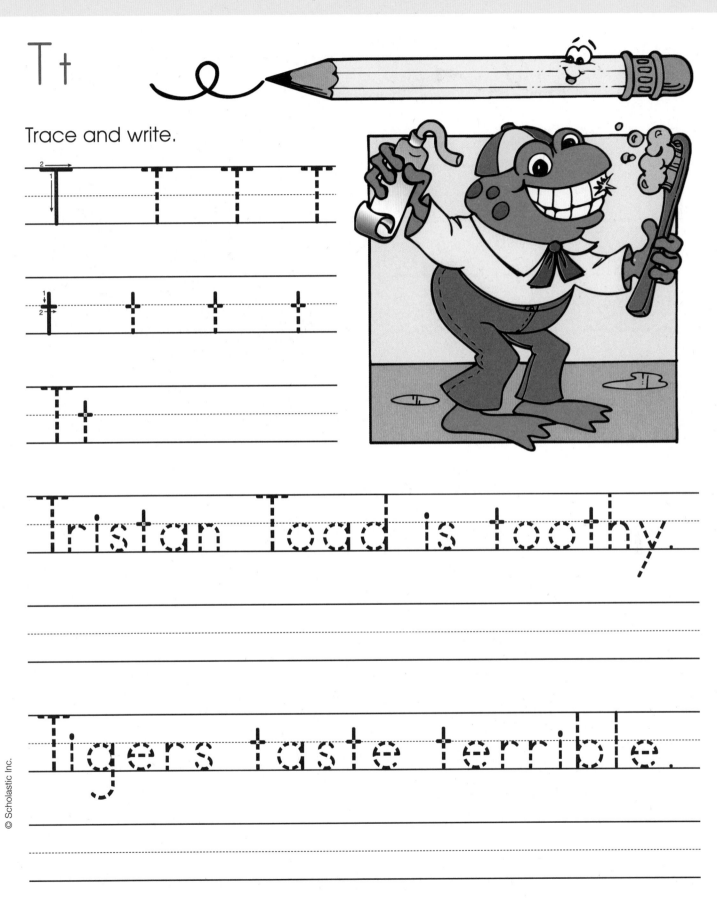

Tristan Toad is toothy.

Tigers taste terrible.

Uu

Trace and write.

U U U U U

u u u u u

Uu

Ula uses an umbrella.

Uncle Uno umpires.

V v

Trace and write.

V V V

V V V V

V v

Vic Vulture is vain.

Vegetables vary.

W w

Trace and write.

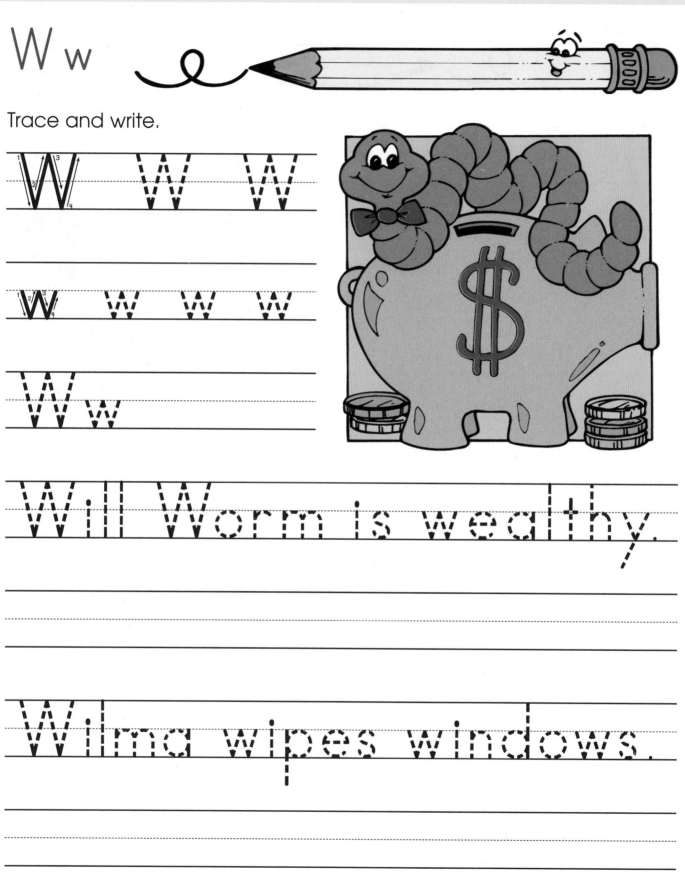

W W W W

w w w w

Ww

Will Worm is wealthy.

Wilma wipes windows.

Xx

Trace and write.

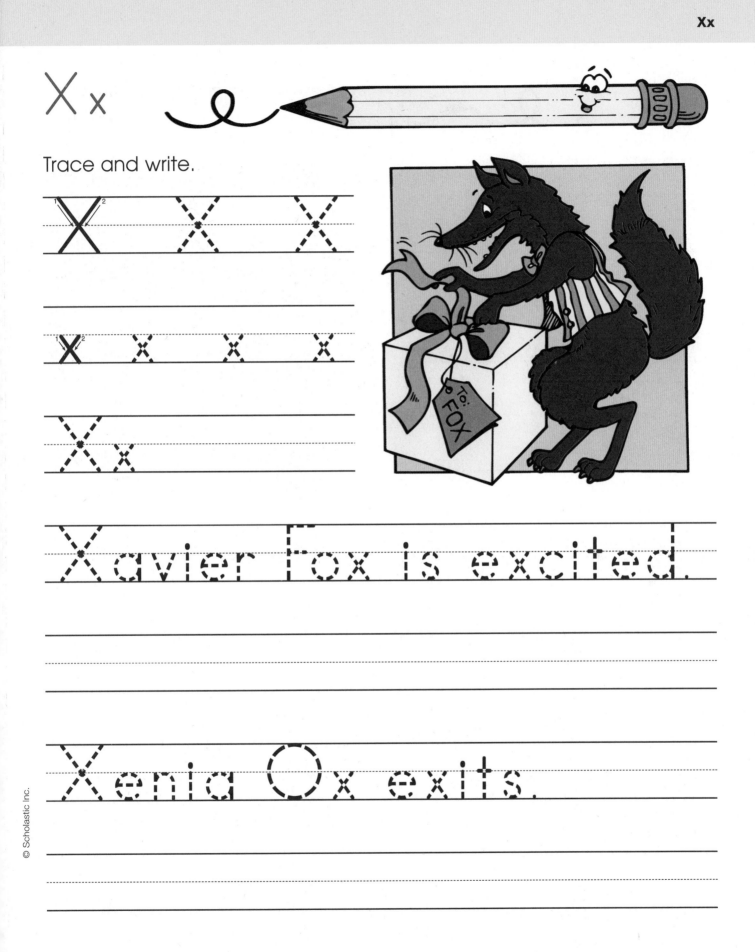

X͟ X X

X X X X

X x

Xavier Fox is excited.

Xenia Ox exits.

Yy

Trace and write.

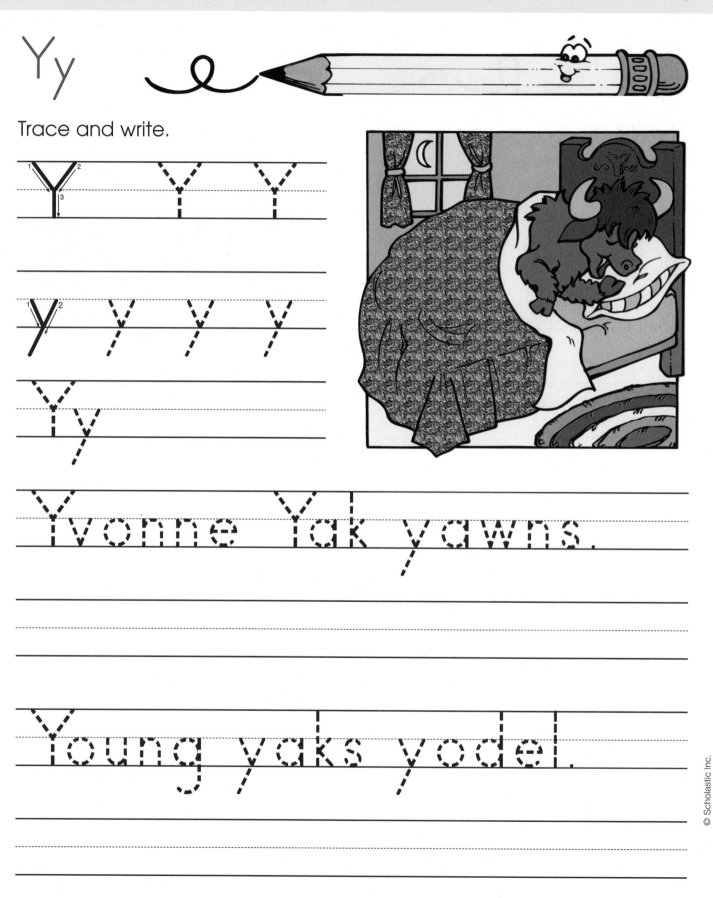

Y Y Y

y y y y

Yy

Yvonne Yak yawns.

Young yaks yodel.

Z z

Trace and write.

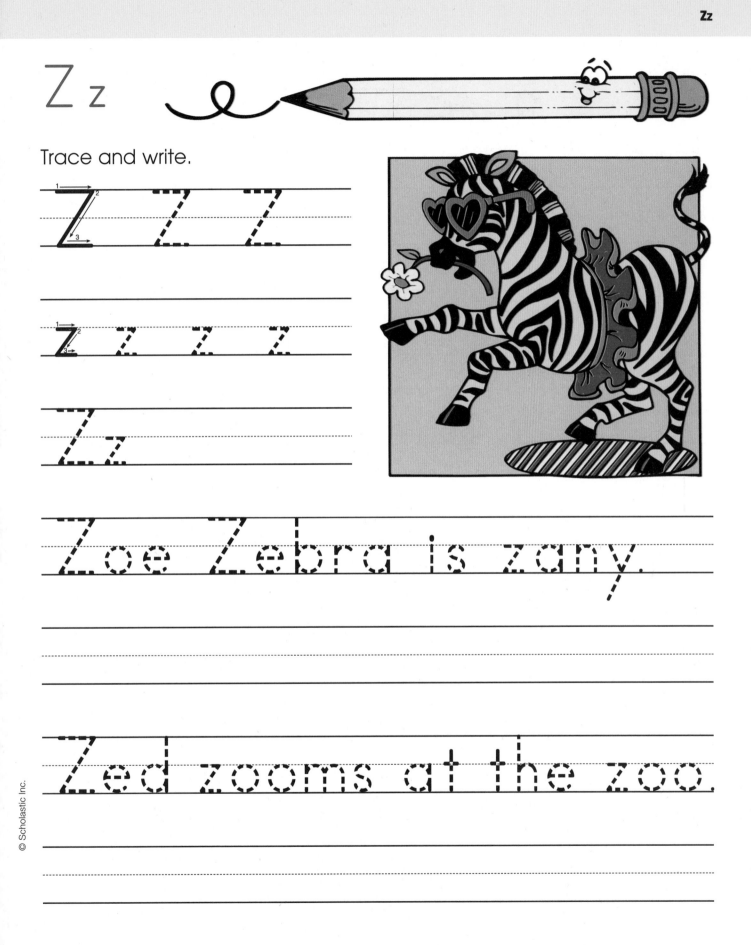

Z Z Z Z Z

Z Z Z Z Z

Z z

Zoe Zebra is zany.

Zed zooms at the zoo.

A–Z

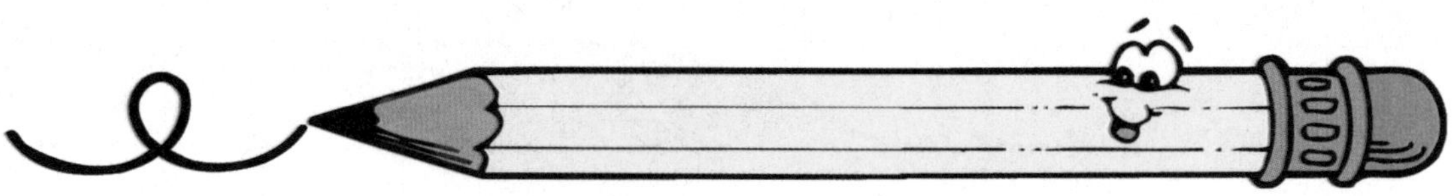

Trace and write.

A B C D E F G H I

J K L M N O P Q

R S T U V W X Y Z

ABCD

a–z

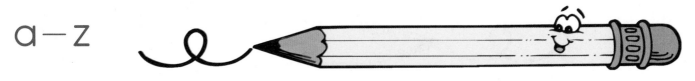

Trace and write.

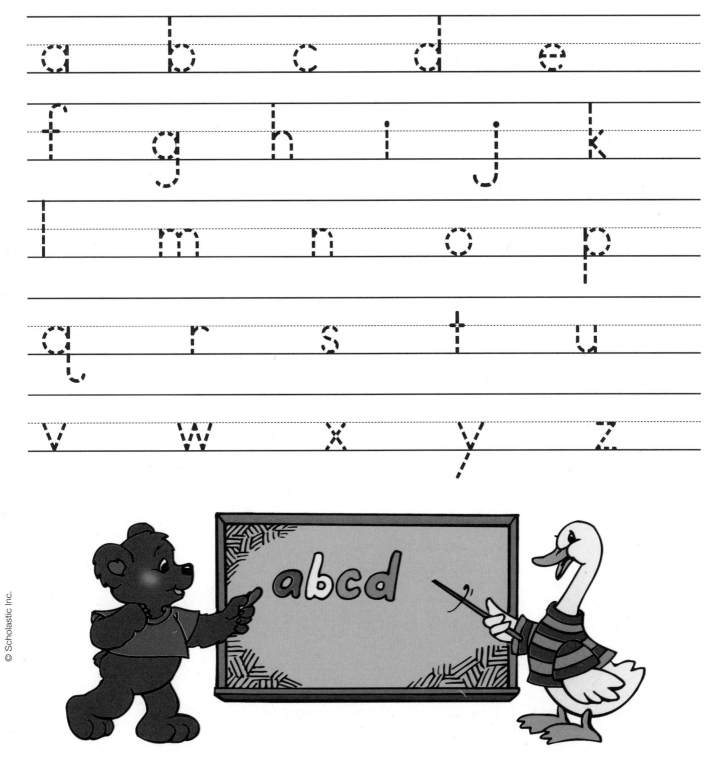

a b c d e

f g h i j k

l m n o p

q r s t u

v w x y z

1–5

Trace and write.

6-10

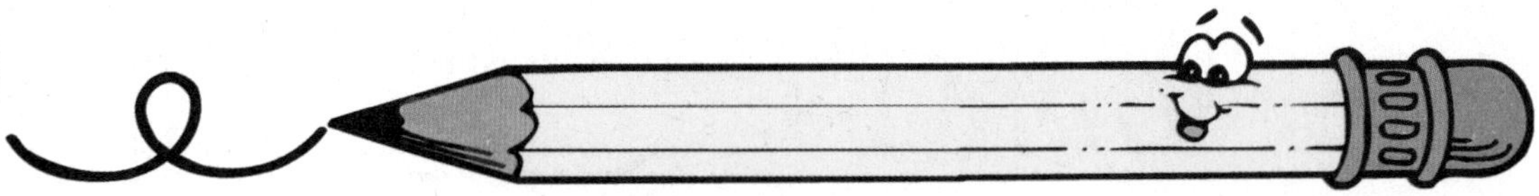

Trace and write.

6 7 8 9 10

6 6

7 7

8 8

9 9

10 10

Color Words

Trace and write.

red

yellow

blue

green

orange

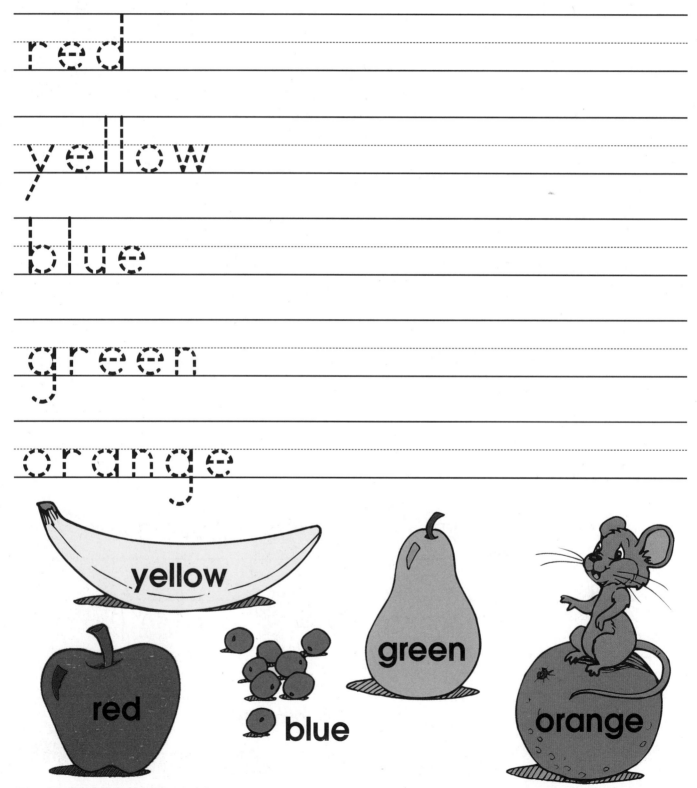

yellow

red

blue

green

orange

More Color Words

Trace and write.

purple

brown

black

white

pink

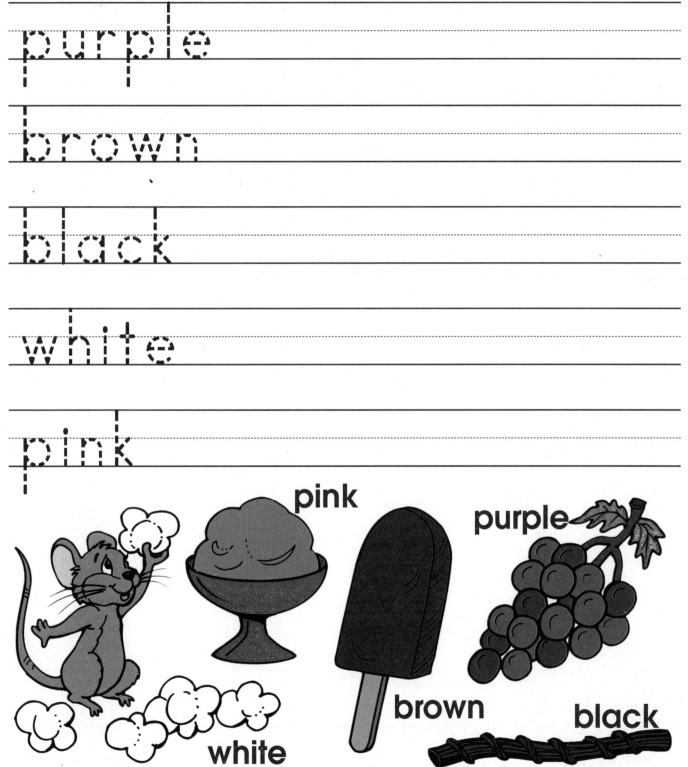

pink

purple

brown

white

black

Number Words

Trace and write.

1 one

2 two

3 three

4 four

5 five

More Number Words

Trace and write.

6 six

7 seven

8 eight

9 nine

10 ten

Shapes

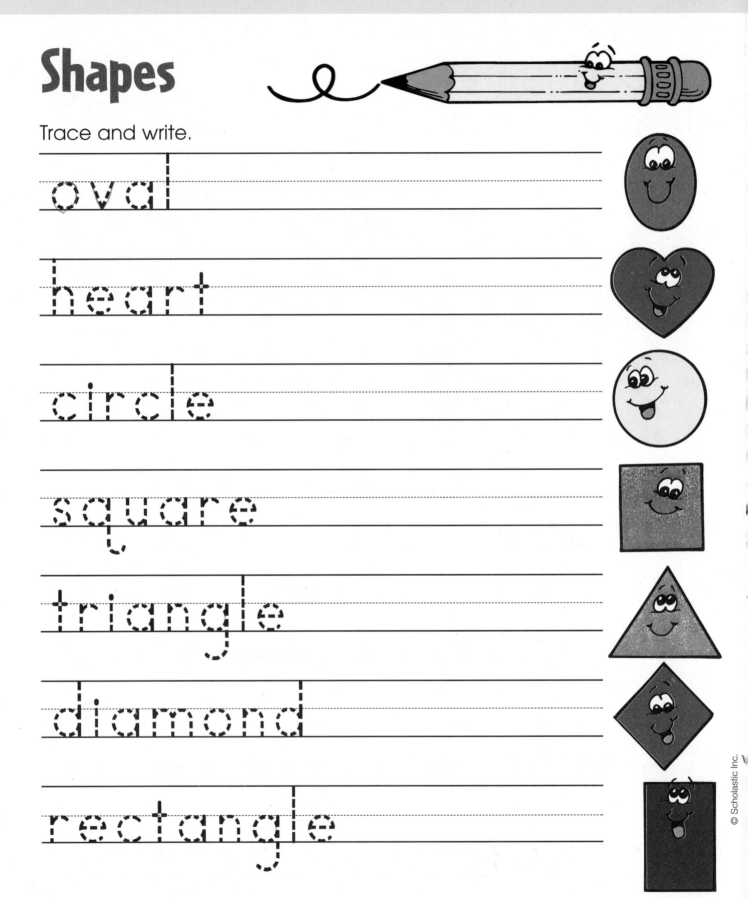

Trace and write.

oval

heart

circle

square

triangle

diamond

rectangle

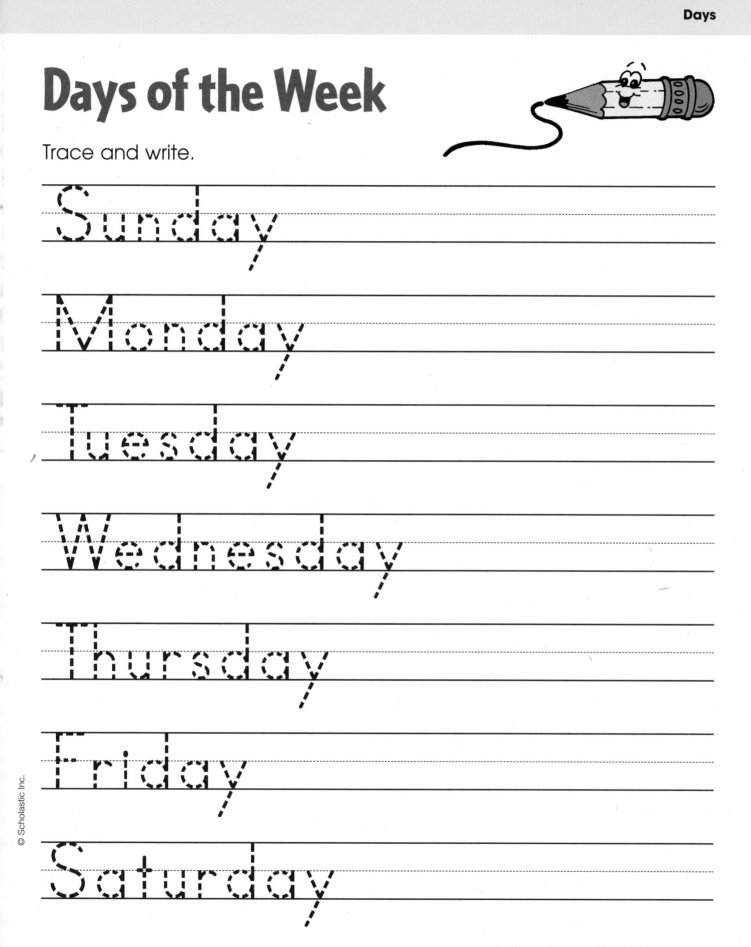

Days of the Week

Trace and write.

Sunday

Monday

Tuesday

Wednesday

Thursday

Friday

Saturday

Months

Trace and write.

January   anuate

February   eruary

March   March March

April   APriA Pril

May   Max Max Max

June   June June June

Months

Trace and write.

July

August

September

October

November

December

Special Days

Write each special day.

JAN | FEB. | MAR | APRIL | MAY | JUN. | JULY

New Year's Day

New Years Day

Valentine's Day

Valentines Day

Presidents' Day

Presidents Day

St. Patrick's Day

St Patricks Day

Mother's Day

Mothers Day

Father's Day

Fathers Day

Fourth of July

Fourth of July

Special Days

Write each special day.

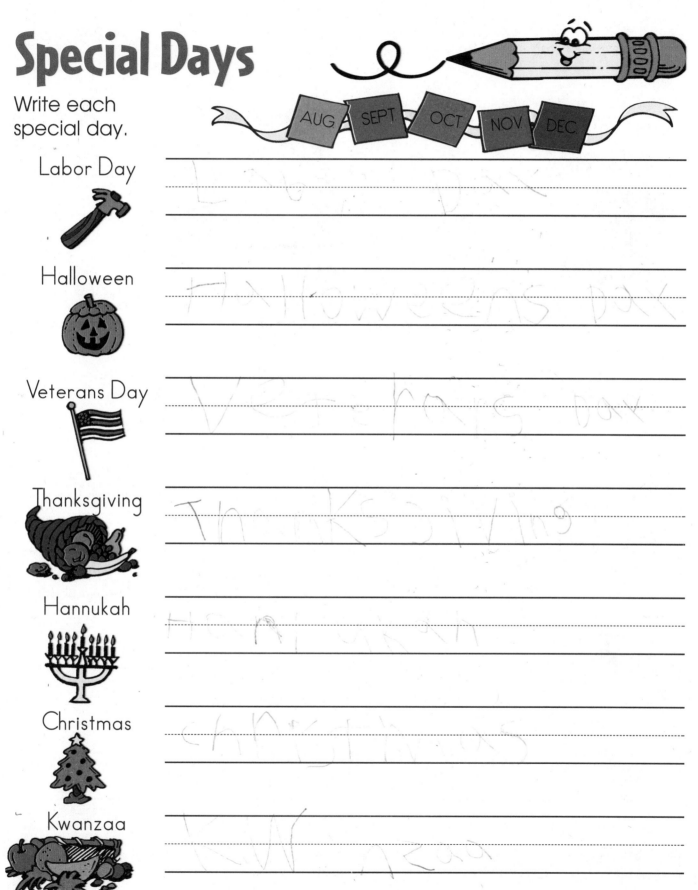

AUG SEPT. OCT NOV. DEC.

Labor Day

Halloween

Veterans Day

Thanksgiving

Hannukah

Christmas

Kwanzaa

© Scholastic Inc.

Animals From A to Z

Write the animal names on the lines below.

alligator
bear
cougar
duck

elk
frog
giraffe
horse

iguana
jaguar
kangaroo
leopard

moose
newt
ostrich

alligatoralligatoralligator

frog frog frog frog frog

giraffe giraffe

iguana iguana iguana

ostrich ostrich ostrich

Animals From A to Z

Write the animal names on the lines below.

parrot
quail
raccoon

squirrel
tiger
urchin

vulture
whale
X-ray fish

yak
zebra

ParrotParrotParrot

raccoonraccoonraccoon

squirrelsquirrelsquirrel

vulturevulture

zebrazebrazebrazebra

The Continents

Write the names of the continents.

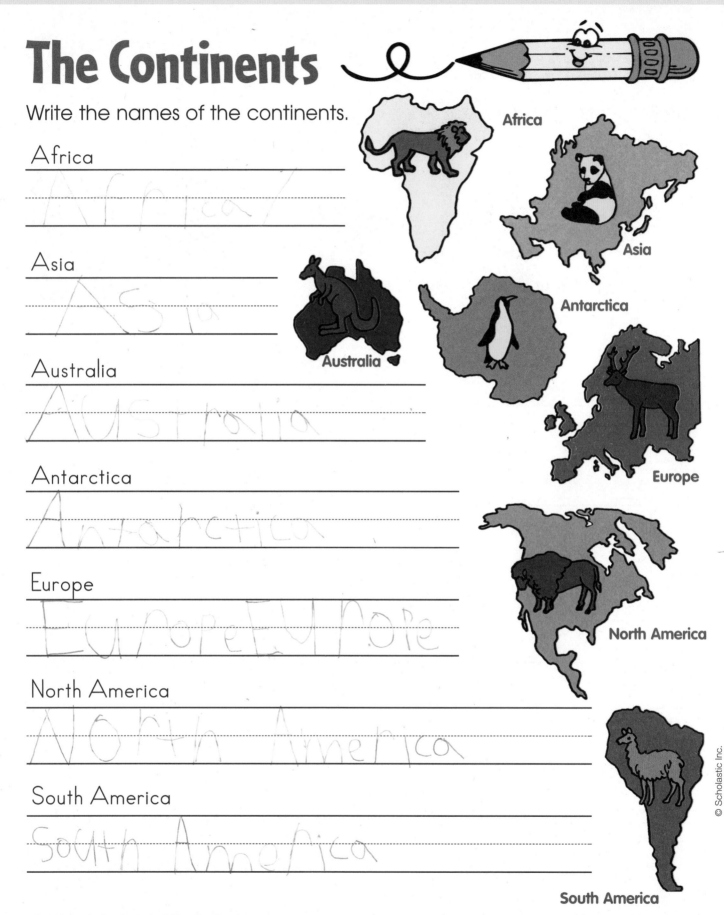

Africa

Africa

Asia

Asia

Australia

Australia

Antarctica

Antarctica

Europe

EuropeEurope

North America

North America

South America

South America

Africa

Asia

Antarctica

Australia

Europe

North America

South America

The Planets

Write the names of these planets.

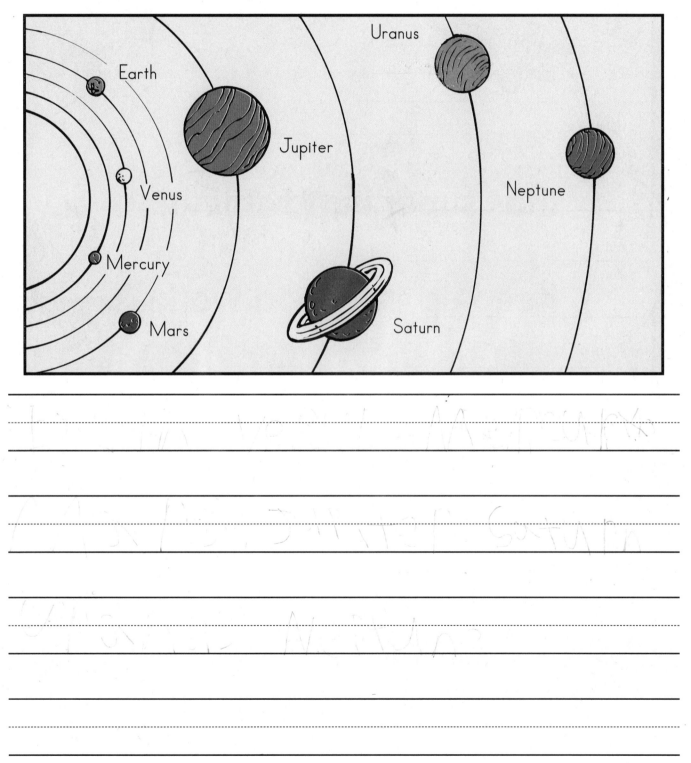

_____

_____

_____

_____

_____

_____

has super handwriting!

Keep up the good work!

_____
signed

_____
date

GRAMMAR

Capitalizing First Word

 *A sentence always begins with a capital letter.*

Draw a line under the first letter in each sentence.
Read each sentence to a friend.

1 The cat sat on a rat.

2 The rat sat on a hat.

3 The hat is on the dog.

4 The dog is on a mat.

© Scholastic Inc.

Capitalizing First Word

A sentence always begins with a capital letter.

Copy each sentence correctly on the line.

1 the cat sat.

2 the dog sat.

3 i see the cat.

4 i can see.

Capitalizing First Word

Read each sentence. Then fill in the circle next to the word with the capital letter that begins the sentence.

1 The cat is in the van.
- ⬭ cat
- ⬭ The

2 My dog can run.
- ⬭ My
- ⬭ dog

3 Jan can hop.
- ⬭ Jan
- ⬭ hop

4 I like ham.
- ⬭ ham
- ⬭ I

5 Ants like jam.
- ⬭ jam
- ⬭ Ants

© Scholastic Inc.

Periods

 *A telling sentence ends with a period.*

Circle the period at the end of each sentence.

1 I see Jan.　　　　**2** I go with Jan.

3 We see Dan.　　　**4** I go with Dan and Jan.

Draw a line under the last word in each sentence.
Add a period to each sentence.

5 We go to school　　**6** We like school

Periods

 A telling sentence ends with a period.

Write a period where it belongs in each sentence. Read the sentences to a friend.

1 Dan is in the cab

2 The cat is in the cab

3 Mom is in the cab

4 We see Dan and Mom

Read the words. Write each word at the end of the correct sentence.

| van.   red. |

5 We can go in the _____

6 The van is _____

Periods

Read each group of words. Fill in the circle next to the correct sentence.

1
- ⬭ The cat is on the mat.
- ⬭ the cat is on the mat
- ⬭ the cat on the mat

2
- ⬭ the rat is on the mop
- ⬭ the rat is on the mop
- ⬭ The rat is on the mop.

3
- ⬭ The rat sees the cat
- ⬭ The rat sees the cat.
- ⬭ the rat sees the cat

4
- ⬭ The rat can hop.
- ⬭ The rat can hop
- ⬭ the rat can hop

5
- ⬭ the cat and rat sit
- ⬭ The cat and rat sit
- ⬭ The cat and rat sit.

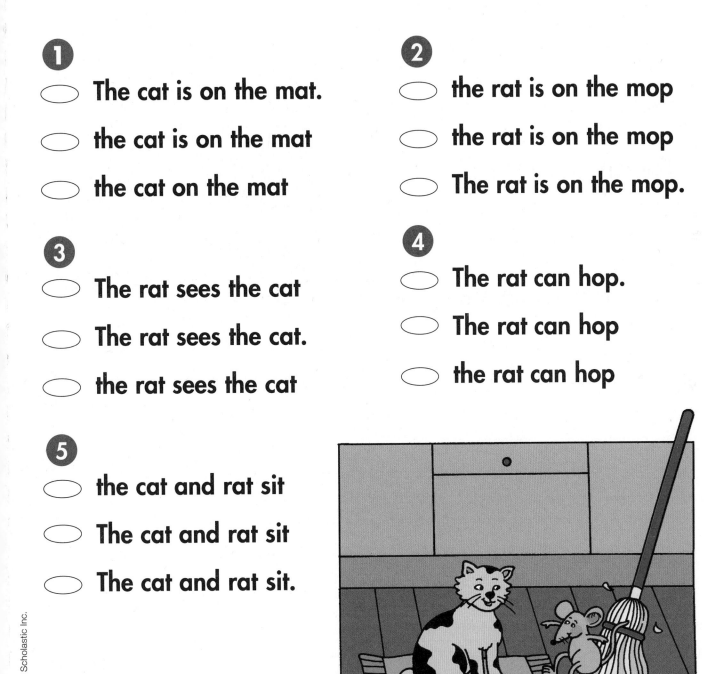

Capitalizing I

Always write the word I with a capital letter.

Circle the word **I** in each sentence.

1 I like to hop.

2 Pam and I like to hop.

3 I can hop to Mom.

4 Mom and I can hop.

Draw what you like. Use the word **I** to write about it.

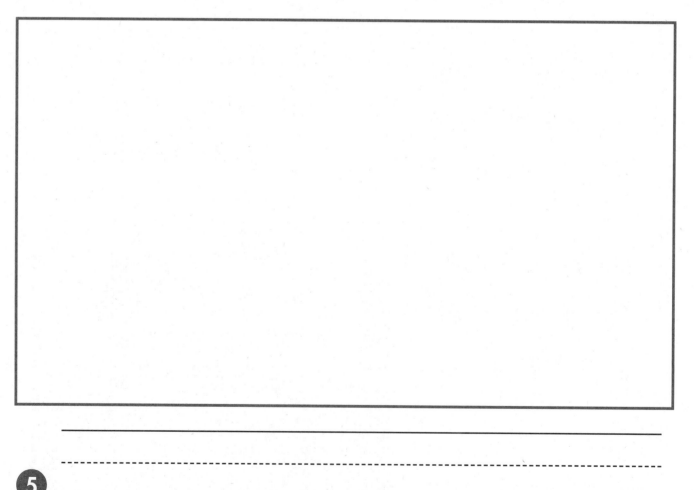

5 _____

Capitalizing I

Always write the word I with a capital letter.

Read the sentences. Write **I** on the line.

1 _____ will ride.

2 _____ will swim.

3 Mom and _____ will sing.

4 Then _____ will read.

What will you do next? Write it on the line.

5 I will

Capitalizing I

Read each group of words. Fill in the circle next to the correct sentence.

1
- ⬭ i sit on a mat.
- ⬭ I sit on a mat.
- ⬭ i sit on a mat

2
- ⬭ Pam and I like cats.
- ⬭ Pam and i like cats.
- ⬭ pam and i like cats

3
- ⬭ I see the van.
- ⬭ i see the van.
- ⬭ i see the van

4
- ⬭ i like jam.
- ⬭ i like jam
- ⬭ I like jam.

5
- ⬭ i like to nap.
- ⬭ I like to nap.
- ⬭ i like to nap

Simple Sentences

 A sentence tells a complete idea.

Circle who or what each sentence is about.

1 **Pam ran.**

2 **Dan hops.**

3 **The cat sits.**

4 **The van can go.**

Draw a line from each sentence to the picture
of who or what the sentence is about.

5 **Jan is hot.**

6 **The hat is on top.**

7 **The man sat.**

Simple Sentences

 A sentence tells a complete idea.

Circle each sentence.

1 **Bill**
Bill paints.

2 **likes to read**
Tom likes to read.

3 **plants flowers**
Pat plants flowers.

Finish the sentence.

4 I like _____

Simple Sentences

Read each group of words. Fill in the circle next to the complete sentence.

1

- ⬭ on a mat
- ⬭ The cat sits on a mat.
- ⬭ The cat

2

- ⬭ Pam and Dan like jam.
- ⬭ Pam and Dan
- ⬭ like jam

3

- ⬭ I see Mom.
- ⬭ I see
- ⬭ Mom

4

- ⬭ my hat
- ⬭ I like
- ⬭ I like my hat.

5

- ⬭ Ben.
- ⬭ Ben can hop.
- ⬭ hop

Word Order

 Words in a sentence must be in an order that makes sense.

Read each group of words. Draw a line under the word that should go first in each sentence.

1 dots. I like

2 Pam dots. likes

3 like We hats.

4 hats with dots. We like

Now write each group of words in the right order.

1 _____

2 _____

3 _____

4 _____

Word Order

 Words in a sentence must be in an order that makes sense.

Read each group of words. Write them in the right order on the lines.

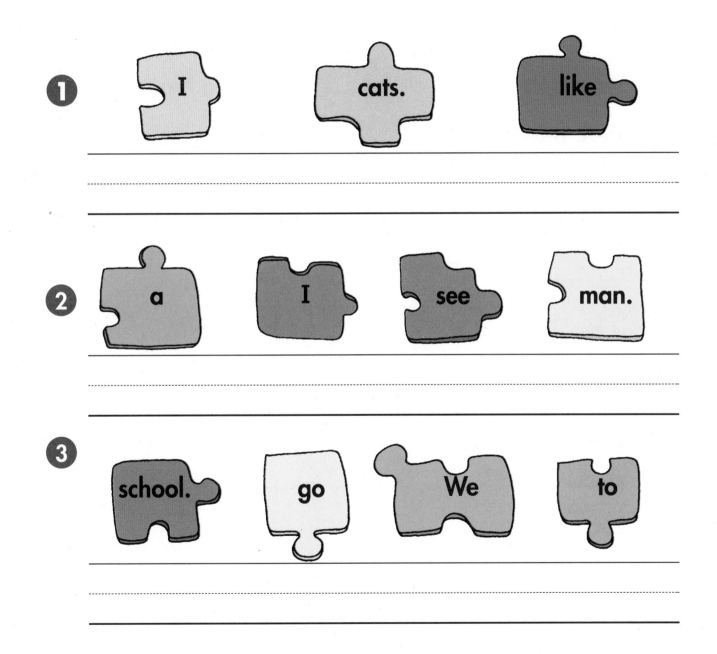

1 I   cats.   like

_____

2 a   I   see   man.

_____

3 school.   go   We   to

_____

Word Order

Read each group of words. Fill in the circle next to the words that are in an order that makes sense.

1
- ⬭ I red dots. see
- ⬭ I see red dots.
- ⬭ dots red

2
- ⬭ Dan is in a big van.
- ⬭ big Dan a van. is in
- ⬭ van big Dan in a is

3
- ⬭ fat. cat The is
- ⬭ is fat. The cat
- ⬭ The cat is fat.

4
- ⬭ We like the hat.
- ⬭ the like hat. We
- ⬭ We hat. the like

5
- ⬭ likes Ben jam.
- ⬭ Ben likes jam.
- ⬭ jam. likes Ben

Question Sentences

Question sentences ask something.

Read each sentence. Circle each question mark.

1 Who hid the hat?

2 Is it on the cat?

3 Can you see the hat?

4 Is it on the man?

Write two questions. Draw a line under each capital letter at the beginning of each question. Circle the question marks.

5 _____

_____

6 _____

_____

Question Sentences

Question sentences ask something.

Draw a line under each sentence that asks a question.
Circle the question mark.

1 Who hid the cat?

2 Can the cat see the rat?

3 The cat is in the van.

4 Can the van go?

Read the sentences. Circle each sentence that asks something.

5 Can we sit in the van?

We can sit in the van.

6 Dan can nap in the van.

Can Dan nap in the van?

Question Sentences

Read the sentences. Fill in the circle next to the sentence that asks a question.

1

○ Who hid my hat?

○ My hat is with him.

○ My hat is big.

2

○ The hat has spots.

○ The hat has dots.

○ Did the hat have dots?

3

○ Jan likes my hat.

○ Did Jan like my hat?

○ Jan did like my hat.

4

○ Can you see the hat?

○ You can see the hat.

○ She can see the hat.

5

○ Dan can get a hat.

○ Dan likes hats.

○ Dan has the hat?

© Scholastic Inc.

Naming Words

A naming word names a person, place, or thing.

Read each sentence. Draw a line under the word or words that name the person, place, or thing in each sentence.

1 The pig is big.

2 The pan is hot.

3 Pam hid.

4 Can you run up the hill?

Draw a line from each sentence to the picture that shows the naming word in that sentence.

5 The sun is hot.

6 Sam ran and ran.

7 Is the cat fat?

Naming Words

A naming word names a person, place, or thing.

Circle the naming words in the sentences.

1 Al can go in a van.

2 The cat sat on a mat.

3 Pat ran up the hill.

4 Dan and Jan will mop.

Draw a picture of a person, place, or thing. Write a sentence about your picture. Circle the naming word.

Naming Words

Read each sentence. Fill in the circle next to the naming word.

1 I see a big cat.

ⓐ see   ⓑ big   ⓒ cat

2 The rat ran fast.

ⓐ ran   ⓑ rat   ⓒ fast

3 Can you see the map?

ⓐ Can   ⓑ map   ⓒ see

4 The van is tan.

ⓐ van   ⓑ is   ⓒ tan

5 The fan is not on!

ⓐ not   ⓑ on   ⓒ fan

Capitalizing Special Names

The names of people, places, and pets are special. They begin with capital letters.

Draw a line under the special name in each sentence. Then circle the first letter or letters in that name.

1 They go to Hill Park.

2 Pam sees the ham.

3 Don sees the cat.

4 They like Frog Lake.

Write a special name of a person, place, or pet you know.

5 _____

Capitalizing Special Names

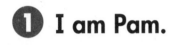 *The names of people, places, and pets are special. They begin with capital letters.*

Circle each special name. Draw a line under each capital letter in each name.

1 I am Pam.

2 I sit on Ant Hill.

3 Ron likes the lake.

4 He likes Bat Lake.

Read the special names in the box.
Write a special name for each picture.

| Spot | Hill Street |

5

6

Capitalizing Special Names

Read each sentence. Fill in the circle next to the special name.

1 Can Don go to the picnic?

- ○ picnic
- ○ Don
- ○ Can

2 The picnic will be on Pig Hill.

- ○ Pig Hill
- ○ picnic
- ○ The

3 The hill is on Jam Street.

- ○ hill
- ○ The
- ○ Jam Street

4 Jan will go to the picnic.

- ○ go
- ○ picnic
- ○ Jan

5 She will go in Ham Lake.

- ○ She
- ○ Ham Lake
- ○ will

Action Words

An action word tells what happens.

Read each sentence. Circle the word that tells what happens.

1 The hen sits.

2 The cat ran.

3 Pam hid.

4 The dog naps.

Read the words. Use the words to finish the sentences.

run	see

_____

5 I will _____ up the hill.

_____

6 I _____ a big pig.

Action Words

An action word tells what happens.

Look at each picture. Read the words. Write the action word.

1   I can see.   _____

2   The cat sits.   _____

3   Mom mops.   _____

4   We run fast.   _____

5   It hops a lot.   _____

Action Words

Read each sentence.
Fill in the circle next to the action word.

1 I sit on a hill.

ⓐ I   ⓑ sit   ⓒ hill

2 The rat ran fast.

ⓐ ran   ⓑ rat   ⓒ fast

3 We mop a lot.

ⓐ We   ⓑ lot   ⓒ mop

4 The dog digs up sand.

ⓐ dog   ⓑ sand   ⓒ digs

5 Pam hops up and down.

ⓐ hops   ⓑ up   ⓒ Pam

Describing Words

A describing word tells more about a person, place, or thing.

Read each sentence. Circle the word that tells about the cat.

1 I see a **big** cat.

2 The **fast** cat ran.

3 My cat is **bad**.

4 The **fat** cat naps.

Look at each cat. Circle the word that tells about it.

5 fat   little

6 big   little

Describing Words

A describing word tells more about a person, place, or thing.

Look at each picture. Circle the words that tell about it.

1

big   fast

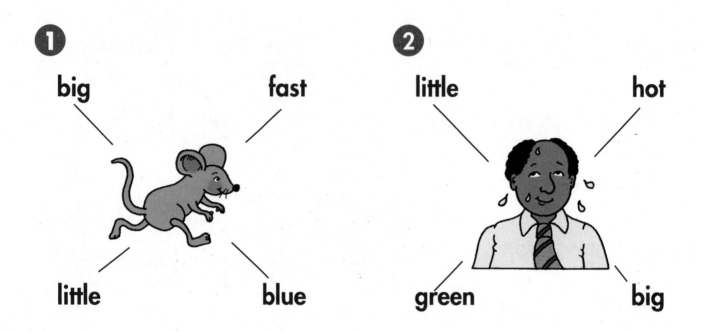

little   blue

2

little   hot

green   big

Draw a line between each sentence and the picture that shows what it describes.

3 It is fat.

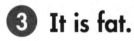

4 They are little.

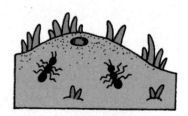

Describing Words

Read each sentence. Fill in the circle next to the describing word.

1 The silly cat can play.

- ⬭ silly
- ⬭ cat
- ⬭ play

2 The bad rat will run.

- ⬭ bad
- ⬭ run
- ⬭ rat

3 The black dog naps.

- ⬭ dog
- ⬭ black
- ⬭ naps

4 The cow is big.

- ⬭ cow
- ⬭ is
- ⬭ big

5 A green frog can hop.

- ⬭ frog
- ⬭ green
- ⬭ hop

Telling Sentences

A telling sentence tells something.

Circle the capital letter at the beginning of each telling sentence.
Then circle the period at the end of each telling sentence.

1 I see the basket.

2 The cat is in the basket.

3 Hats can go in it.

4 The sock can go in it.

Draw a line under each telling sentence.

5 I can fill the basket.

6 Can you get the mop?

7 We can clean.

© Scholastic Inc.

Telling Sentences

 A telling sentence tells something.

Draw a line to match each sentence with the picture that shows what the sentence tells.

1 **She has a mop.**

2 **The dog is on top.**

3 **Dan gets the hats.**

4 **Ron can clean spots.**

Read the sentences. Circle the capital letter and period in the telling sentence.

5 **Put it in the pot.**   **6** **Is it in the pan?**

Telling Sentences

Read the sentences. Fill in the circle next to each sentence that tells something.

1

○ Can you get the basket?

○ You can get it.

○ Can you fill it?

2

○ The basket is big.

○ Is the basket big?

○ Why is it big?

3

○ What can go in it?

○ Will the hat go in?

○ The hat is in the basket.

4

○ A cat can not go in it.

○ Can a cat go in?

○ Will a cat go in it?

5

○ Can we fill it?

○ We can fill the basket.

○ Will you fill it?

© Scholastic Inc.

Exclamation Sentences

Exclamatory sentences show strong feelings such as excitement, surprise, or fear. They end with exclamation marks. (!)

Read each sentence. Circle each exclamation mark. Draw a line under the capital letter at the beginning of each sentence.

1 **Help! The rat is on top!**

2 **Get the cat!**

3 **This cat is bad!**

4 **Uh-oh! The cat is wet!**

Read each set of sentences. Draw a line under the sentence or sentences that show strong feeling.

5 **Oh my! Get the dog!**

Let's get the dog.

6 **The dog runs.**

Oh! The dog runs!

© Scholastic Inc.

Exclamation Sentences

Choose the sentence in each pair that shows strong feeling. Write it on the line. Put an exclamation mark at the end.

> Exclamatory sentences show strong feeling, such as excitement, surprise, or fear.
> They end with an exclamation mark. (!)

1 Run to the show   We will go to the show

_____

- -

_____

2 I'm late for it   Oh my, I'm very late

_____

- -

_____

3 What a great show   I liked the show

_____

- -

_____

4 The floor is wet   Watch out, the floor is wet

_____

- -

_____

5 We had fun   Wow, we had lots of fun

_____

- -

_____

Exclamation Sentences

Read each group of sentences. Fill in the circle next to the sentence or sentences that show strong feeling.

1
- ◯ The cow is on the hill.
- ◯ The cow likes grass.
- ◯ Yes! The cow can kick!

2
- ◯ That cat is bad!
- ◯ That cat naps.
- ◯ Is the cat on the mat?

3
- ◯ The rat will run.
- ◯ That rat runs fast!
- ◯ The rat can hop.

4
- ◯ Oh no! A frog is in my house!
- ◯ A frog hops.
- ◯ The frog is green.

5
- ◯ The pot can get hot.
- ◯ The pot is hot!
- ◯ Fill the pot with mud.

Punctuation Power

Each sentence is missing a punctuation mark.
Draw a line to match each punctuation mark to a sentence.

1 Let's go

2 I am a kid

3 Why doesn't the clock work

4 Do you have a hat

5 This game is fun

6 I play soccer

7 What's your name

8 The beach is great

9 My name is Paul

!

?

.

!

?

.

!

?

Singular/Plural Nouns

Many nouns, or naming words, add -s to show more than one.

Read each sentence. Draw a line under each naming word that means more than one.

1 I see hats and a cap.

2 It sits on eggs.

3 The girls swim.

4 Pam can pet cats.

Read each sentence. Write the naming word that means more than one.

_____

5 The mugs are hot. _____

_____

6 Mud is on my hands. _____

Singular/Plural Nouns

Many nouns, or naming words, add -s to show more than one.

Read the sets of sentences. Draw a line under the sentence that has a naming word that names more than one.

1 Jan has her mittens.

Jan has her mitten.

2 She will run up a hill.

She will run up hills.

3 Jan runs with her dogs.

Jan runs with her dog.

4 The dogs can jump.

The dog can jump.

Look at each picture. Read each word. Write the plural naming word that matches the picture.

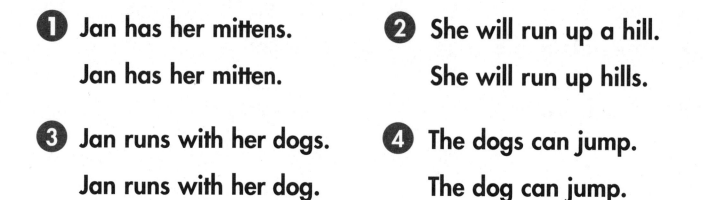

5 cat _____

6 sock _____

Singular/Plural Nouns

Read each sentence. Fill in the circle next to the naming word that means more than one.

1 Jim gets mud on his hands.

- ◯ gets
- ◯ hands
- ◯ mud

2 Pam can fill the pots with mud.

- ◯ pots
- ◯ mud
- ◯ fill

3 The dogs dig fast.

- ◯ dig
- ◯ fast
- ◯ dogs

4 The ants are on the plant.

- ◯ ants
- ◯ plant
- ◯ are

5 The frogs hop.

- ◯ The
- ◯ frogs
- ◯ hop

Action Words

 *An action word tells what happens.*

Read each sentence. Circle the word that tells what happens.

1 The hen sits.
2 Mom sees the hen.

3 The dog digs.
4 The cat naps.

Read the words. Use the words to finish the sentences.

| sees | run |

5 She _____ eggs.

6 It can _____ fast.

Action Words

An action word tells what happens.

Look at the pictures. Read the action words in the box.
Write the correct action word on the line.

talk
play
dance
run

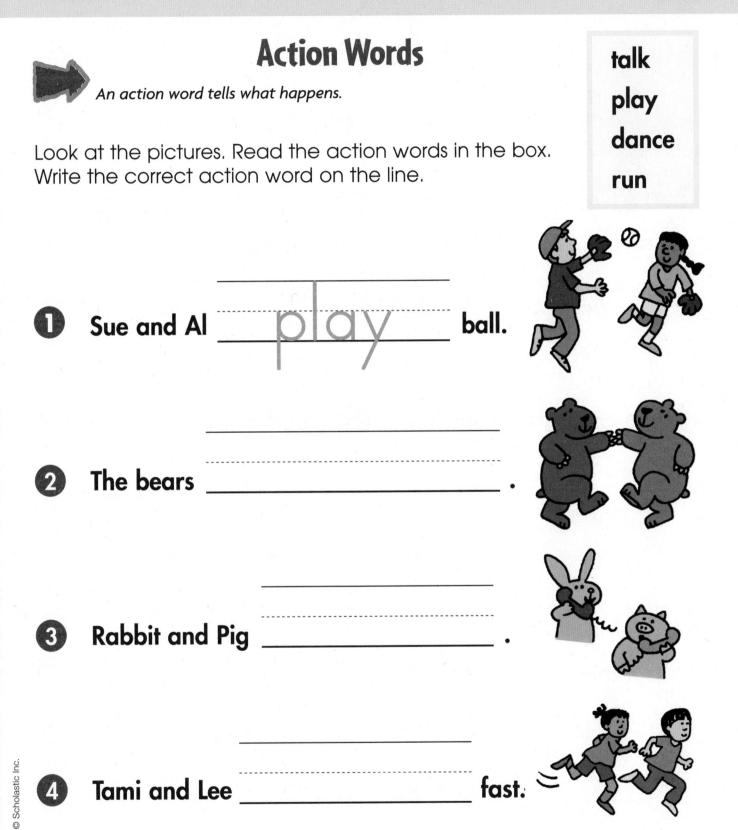

1 Sue and Al __play__ ball.

2 The bears _____ .

3 Rabbit and Pig _____ .

4 Tami and Lee _____ fast.

Action Words

Read each sentence. Fill in the circle next to the action word.

1 **The hen sits.**

- ⬭ hen
- ⬭ sits
- ⬭ The

2 **The cat naps in the van.**

- ⬭ naps
- ⬭ cat
- ⬭ van

3 **The green frog hops.**

- ⬭ frog
- ⬭ green
- ⬭ hops

4 **The dog digs.**

- ⬭ digs
- ⬭ dog
- ⬭ The

5 **The big pig ran.**

- ⬭ big
- ⬭ pig
- ⬭ ran

Naming Words

A naming word names a person, place, or thing.

Read each sentence. Draw a line under the naming word.

1 We play at school.

2 The ball is fast.

3 The girl kicks.

4 The friends run.

Look at each box. Circle the naming word that belongs in that box.

Person	Place	Thing
girl	ball	Pam
school	Bill	man
ball	school	ball

Naming Words

 A naming word names a person, place, or thing.

Read each sentence. Circle each naming word. Draw a line to match the sentence to the picture of the naming word.

1 Run and kick in the park.

2 Kick with a foot.

3 Kick the ball.

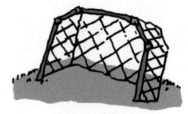

4 The girl will run to get it.

5 Kick it to the net.

Naming Words

Read each sentence. Fill in the circle next to the word that names a person, place, or thing.

1 Let's play in the park.

- ⬭ play
- ⬭ Let's
- ⬭ park

2 The girl can run and kick.

- ⬭ girl
- ⬭ run
- ⬭ kick

3 Kick the ball.

- ⬭ ball
- ⬭ the
- ⬭ kick

4 The friend can jump.

- ⬭ can
- ⬭ jump
- ⬭ friend

5 Jump to the net.

- ⬭ get
- ⬭ net
- ⬭ jump

Word Order

Words in a sentence must be in an order that makes sense.

Read each group of words. Circle the words that are in an order that makes sense. Draw a line under each capital letter.

1 The king is sad.

   sad. king is The

2 bake Let's cake. him a

   Let's bake him a cake.

3 the king Tell to come.

   Tell the king to come.

4 Let's eat the cake.

   eat Let's the cake.

Read the words. Write them in order.

king The eats .

_____

- -

_____

Word Order

Words in a sentence must be in an order that makes sense.

These words are mixed up. Put them in order.
Then write each sentence.

1 snow.   bear   likes   This

2 water   cold.   The   is

3 fast.   The   runs   bear

4 play.   bears   Two

Word Order

Read each group of words. Then fill in the circle next to the words that are in an order that makes sense.

1
- ⬭ Pam will bake a cake.
- ⬭ bake Pam a will cake.
- ⬭ will Pam cake. a bake

2
- ⬭ will king. the see Pam
- ⬭ king. Pam see will the
- ⬭ Pam will see the king.

3
- ⬭ duck. The king has a
- ⬭ The king has a duck.
- ⬭ has a king The duck.

4
- ⬭ lake. the in is The duck
- ⬭ The duck is in the lake.
- ⬭ The lake. duck in is the

5
- ⬭ The king will eat cake.
- ⬭ king will The cake. eat
- ⬭ cake. king will The eat

Capitalizing Titles

 Important words in a title are capitalized.

Circle all the words that are capitalized.

What to See at Night

The Light of the Moon

★ See Many Stars! ★

The Sun and the Moon

Now use some of the words from the titles above to write your own titles.

_____

- -

_____

_____

- -

_____

Capitalizing Titles

Important words in a title are capitalized.

Read the titles. Circle all the words that should be capitalized.

1 look at the stars!

2 the moon shines at night

3 we see planets

4 many moons shine

5 night and day

Read each set of titles. Draw a line under the correct title.

6 The Sun in the Sky

the sun in the sky

7 See the stars!

See the Stars!

Capitalizing Titles

Read the titles. Fill in the circle next to the title with the correct words capitalized.

1
- ⬭ Where Is the Sun?
- ⬭ Where is the sun?
- ⬭ Where Is The Sun?

2
- ⬭ many cats to see
- ⬭ Many cats To See
- ⬭ Many Cats to See

3
- ⬭ Day and Night
- ⬭ day And night
- ⬭ Day And Night

4
- ⬭ how many pigs?
- ⬭ How Many Pigs?
- ⬭ How many pigs?

5
- ⬭ the Big Bad wolf
- ⬭ the big, bad wolf
- ⬭ The Big, Bad Wolf

© Scholastic Inc.

Naming Words

 A naming word names a person, place, or thing.

Read each sentence. Draw a line under the word or words that name the person, place, or thing in each sentence.

1 The pot is big.

2 The pan is big.

3 See the top?

4 Jim can mop.

Draw a line from each sentence to the picture that shows the naming word in that sentence.

5 The pot is hot.

6 See the pan?

7 Jim is fast.

Naming Words

A naming word names a person, place, or thing.

Circle the naming words in the sentences.

1 Jan can go in a van.

2 The van can go fast.

3 The van is on a hill.

4 Dan sees Jan.

Draw a picture of a person, place, or thing.
Write a sentence about your picture.
Circle the naming word.

5

Naming Words

Read each sentence. Fill in the circle next to the naming word.

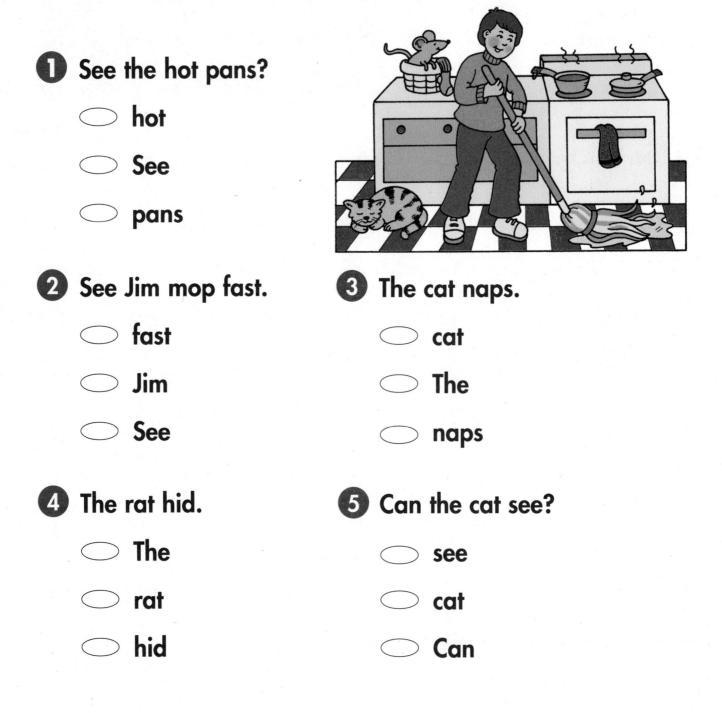

1 See the hot pans?

- ○ hot
- ○ See
- ○ pans

2 See Jim mop fast.

- ○ fast
- ○ Jim
- ○ See

3 The cat naps.

- ○ cat
- ○ The
- ○ naps

4 The rat hid.

- ○ The
- ○ rat
- ○ hid

5 Can the cat see?

- ○ see
- ○ cat
- ○ Can

Linking Verbs

 Is, *are*, *was*, and *were* are linking verbs. *Is* tells about one. *Are* tells about more than one. *Was* tells about one in the past. *Were* tells about more than one in the past.

Read each sentence. Draw a line under the linking verb *is*, *are*, *was*, or *were*.

1 The hen is digging.

2 The chicks were helping.

3 The pig was having fun.

4 The cat and duck are playing.

Read each sentence. Circle *now* or *in the past* to show when it happens or happened.

5 The hen is planting.   now   in the past

6 The cat was not helping.   now   in the past

7 The chicks are with the hen.   now   in the past

Linking Verbs

Is, are, was, and *were* are linking verbs. *Is* tells about one. *Are* tells about more than one. *Was* tells about one in the past. *Were* tells about more than one in the past.

Circle the linking verb. Write <u>now</u> or <u>past</u> to tell when the action happens or happened.

1 The chicks are eating. _____

2 The duck is swimming. _____

3 The cat was napping. _____

4 The pig is digging. _____

5 They were playing. _____

Linking Verbs

Fill in the circle next to the linking verb that completes each sentence.

1 The hen ___ sitting.
- ⭕ was
- ⭕ are
- ⭕ were

2 They ___ playing.
- ⭕ were
- ⭕ is
- ⭕ was

3 The pigs ___ digging.
- ⭕ was
- ⭕ is
- ⭕ are

4 The duck ___ swimming.
- ⭕ were
- ⭕ is
- ⭕ are

5 The chicks ___ napping.
- ⭕ was
- ⭕ is
- ⭕ are

Capitalizing Names and First Words

The first word in a sentence starts with a capital letter. Sometimes words that name a person, place, or thing begin with a capital letter.

Read the sentences. Circle the words that are capitalized.

1 The goats Gruff have a problem.

2 They do not like the Troll.

3 His name is Nosey.

4 He is big and bad.

Draw a line to match each sentence to why the underlined word is capitalized.

5 Dan and <u>Pam</u> like the play.

6 <u>They</u> will read it to Jim.

First word in a sentence.

Names a person, place, or thing.

Capitalizing Names

Sometimes the names of people, places, and things are special.
They begin with a capital letter.

Circle the special names in the picture. Write each one correctly on a line.

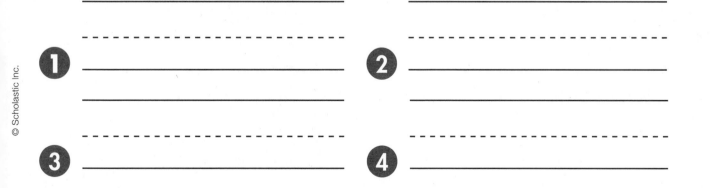

1 _____

2 _____

3 _____

4 _____

Capitalizing Names and First Words

Read each sentence. Fill in the circle next to the word that needs a capital letter.

1 i like the goats Gruff.

- ⬭ Goats
- ⬭ The
- ⬭ I

2 I read the story with ron.

- ⬭ Read
- ⬭ Story
- ⬭ Ron

3 Little gruff had a problem.

- ⬭ Had
- ⬭ Gruff
- ⬭ Problem

4 troll was on the bridge.

- ⬭ A
- ⬭ Bridge
- ⬭ Troll

5 His name was nosey.

- ⬭ Name
- ⬭ Nosey
- ⬭ His

Scholastic Success With

WRITING

That's Amazing!

*A sentence begins with a **capital letter**.*

Help the mouse through the maze by coloring each box with a word that begins with a capital letter.

The	For	That	with	know	but
here	on	When	Have	next	we
as	after	good	Make	there	see
Go	Look	Are	Could	is	why
This	who	said	in	come	them
Has	Name	Before	Her	Where	The

 Read the back of a cereal box. How many capital letters did you find? Write the number next to the cheese.

© Scholastic Inc.

Squeak!

Circle the words that show the correct way to begin each sentence.

1. The mouse
   the mouse
   is looking for food.

2. he finds
   He finds
   a cracker on the floor.

3. he Eats
   He eats
   the cracker.

4. Then he
   then He
   takes a nap.

5. oh No,
   Oh no,
   he hears a cat!

6. the Mouse
   The mouse
   runs home fast!

Counting Sheep

Write the beginning words correctly to make a sentence.

1. we read   _____ books before bed.

2. then we   _____ hug good night.

3. my bed   _____ is soft and cozy.

4. my cat   _____ sleeps with me.

5. the sky   _____ has turned dark.

6. my eyes   _____ close.

On another piece of paper, copy a sentence from your favorite bedtime book. Circle the capital letter at the beginning.

Sweet Dreams!

Write each beginning word correctly to make
a sentence.

1. my
   dog
   _____ runs in her sleep.

2. she
   must
   _____ be dreaming.

3. maybe
   she
   _____ is chasing a cat.

4. sometimes
   she
   _____ even barks.

5. i think
   _____ it is funny.

**On another piece of paper, write a sentence about a dream you remember. Circle the
capital letter at the beginning.**

The Night Sky

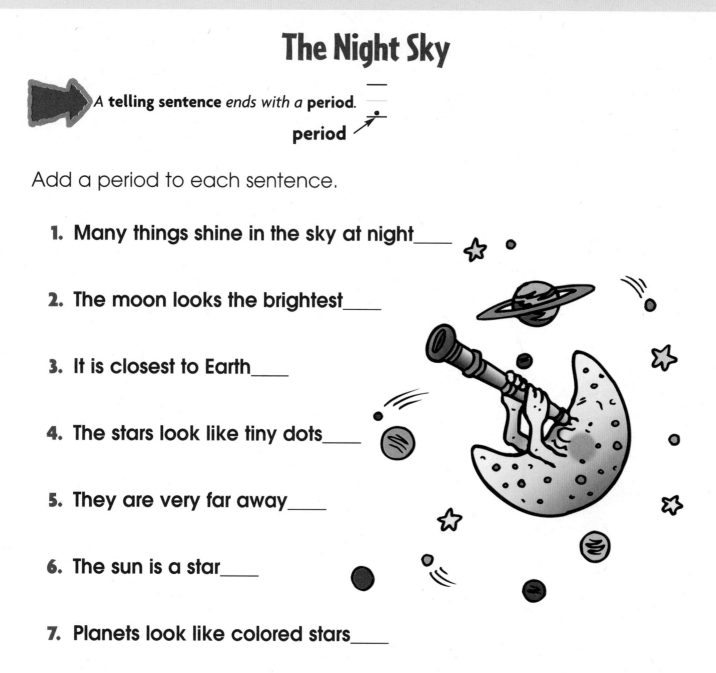

A **telling sentence** *ends with a* **period.**

period

Add a period to each sentence.

1. Many things shine in the sky at night____

2. The moon looks the brightest____

3. It is closest to Earth____

4. The stars look like tiny dots____

5. They are very far away____

6. The sun is a star____

7. Planets look like colored stars____

8. Their light does not twinkle____

9. Shooting stars look like stars that are falling____

10. There are many things to see in the night sky____

© Scholastic Inc.

Twinkle, Twinkle Little Star

Rewrite each sentence using periods.

1. Tonight I saw a star

_____

_____

2. I saw the star twinkle

_____

_____

3. It looked like a candle

_____

_____

4. It was very bright

_____

_____

5. I made a wish

_____

_____

6. I hope it comes true

_____

_____

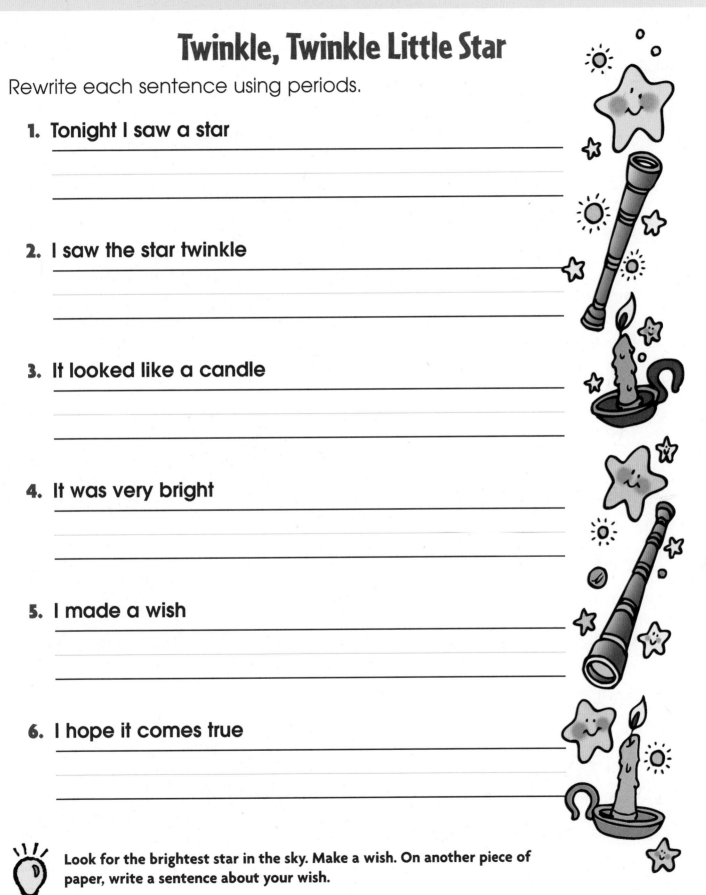

Look for the brightest star in the sky. Make a wish. On another piece of paper, write a sentence about your wish.

Hop to It!

A **telling sentence** *begins with a* **capital letter** *and ends with a* **period**.

Rewrite each sentence correctly.

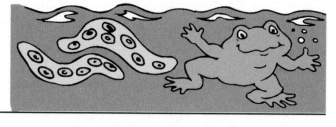

1. frogs and toads lay eggs

_____

_____

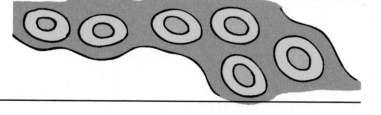

2. the eggs are in the water

_____

_____

3. tadpoles hatch from the eggs

_____

_____

4. the tadpoles grow legs

_____

_____

5. the tadpoles lose their tails

_____

_____

Hop to It Some More!

Rewrite each sentence correctly.

1. tadpoles become frogs or toads

_____

_____

2. frogs live near water

_____

_____

3. toads live mostly on dry land

_____

_____

4. frogs have wet skin

_____

_____

5. toads have bumpy skin

_____

_____

On another piece of paper, write three sentences about a time that you saw a frog or toad. Make sure you use capital letters and periods correctly.

Patriotic Sentences

A **sentence** *tells a complete idea. It should always make sense.*

Color the flag to show:

RED = sentence   WHITE = not a sentence

	This is a flag.
	The flag
	The flag has stars.
	The stars
	The stars are white.
	The stripes
	The stripes are red.

And white

The stripes are white.

Blue part

The flag has a blue part.

There are

There are 50 stars.

Color the star part of the flag with a blue crayon. Then on another piece of paper, write a complete sentence about your colorful flag.

High-Flying Sentences

Color each flag that tells a complete thought. Leave the other flags blank.

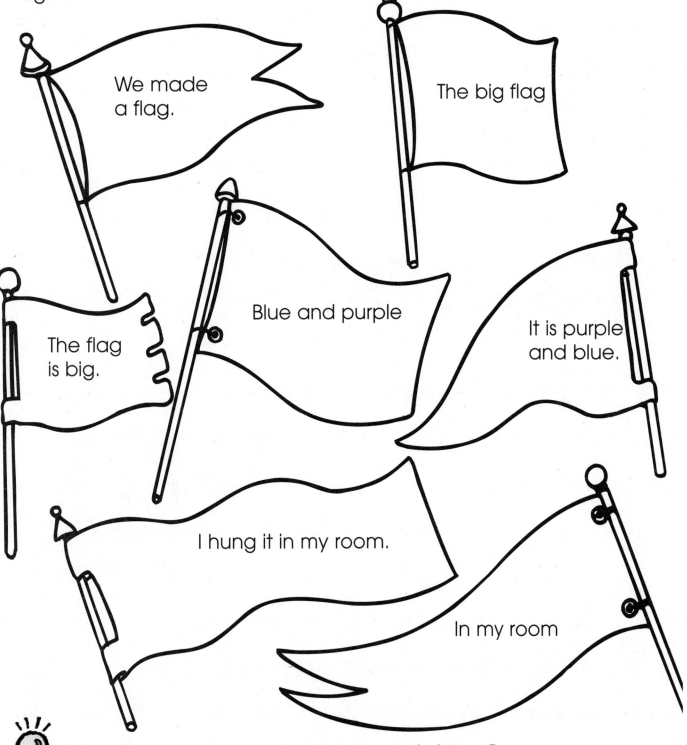

We made a flag.

The big flag

The flag is big.

Blue and purple

It is purple and blue.

I hung it in my room.

In my room

On another piece of paper, turn this into a sentence: **The biggest flag.**

At the Seashore

Unscramble the words to make a sentence. Write the new sentence below each picture. Finish each picture to match the sentence.

sailing are boats Five

four have We buckets

In the Rain Forest

Unscramble the words to make a sentence. Write the new sentence.
Do not forget to put a period at the end.

A hiding jaguar is

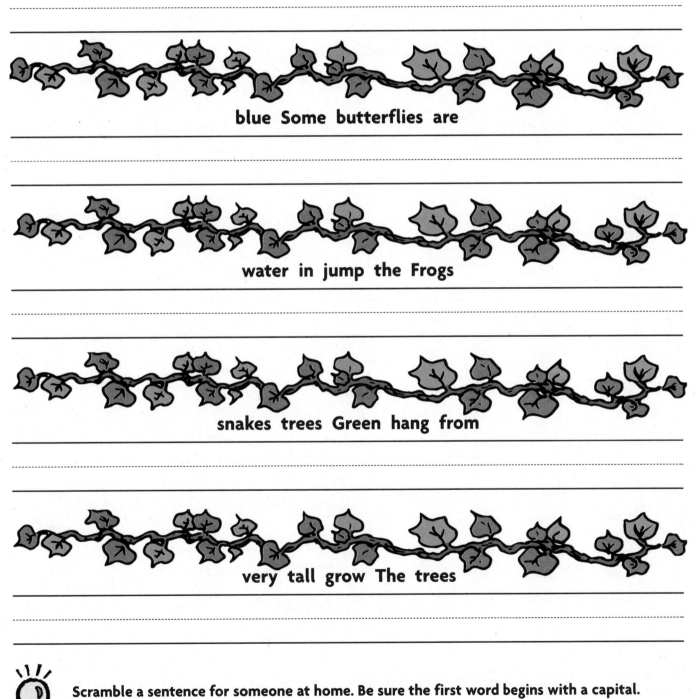

blue Some butterflies are

water in jump the Frogs

snakes trees Green hang from

very tall grow The trees

💡 **Scramble a sentence for someone at home. Be sure the first word begins with a capital.**

Snakes Alive!

*A sentence has a **naming part**. It tells who or what the sentence is about.*

Color the snake that tells the naming part in each sentence below.

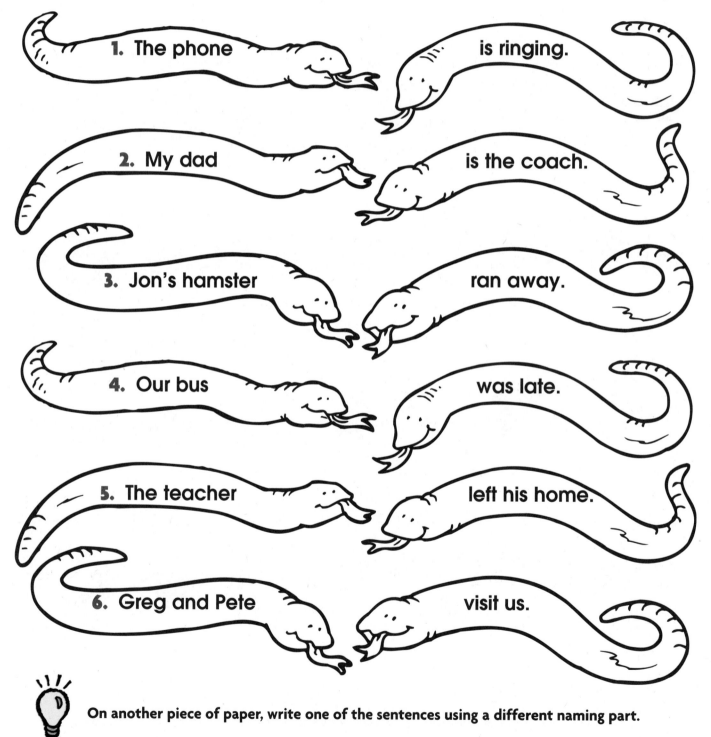

1. The phone   is ringing.

2. My dad   is the coach.

3. Jon's hamster   ran away.

4. Our bus   was late.

5. The teacher   left his home.

6. Greg and Pete   visit us.

On another piece of paper, write one of the sentences using a different naming part.

Slithering Sentences

Circle the naming part in each sentence below.
Then color the picture to match.

1. **The blue snake is playing with a friend.**

2. **The yellow snake is climbing a tree.**

3. **The green snake hides under rocks.**

4. **The brown snake is swimming.**

5. **The red snake is hanging on a tree.**

6. **The purple snake sleeps in trees.**

7. **The black snake rests on a rock.**

8. **The orange snake is near an egg.**

Look around you. On another piece of paper, write three people or things that could be the naming part of a sentence.

Who Is That?

The naming part of a sentence can be a person.

Use the pictures to find naming parts to make each sentence complete.

1. _____ fell on the ice.

2. _____ won the race.

3. _____ went inside the dark cave.

4. _____ climbed the hill.

5. _____ swam across the pool.

© Scholastic Inc.

Where Is That?

The naming part of a sentence can be a place or a thing.

Use naming parts to complete each sentence that tells about the map.

Tree Lane

Park Road

_____

1. _____ is near the swings.

_____

2. _____ is far from the cave.

_____

3. _____ is a good place to fish.

_____

4. _____ has bats inside.

_____

5. _____ is along Tree Lane.

Find the naming part of three sentences in your favorite book.

Family Photos

 *The naming part of a sentence can be a person, a place, or a thing.*

Use your own naming parts to write a complete sentence about each picture.

More Family Photos

Use your own naming parts to write a complete sentence about each picture.

💡 **Look at your family pictures. On another piece of paper, write a sentence telling about two of them.**

No Bones About It!

*A sentence has an **action part**. It tells what is happening.*

Color the bone that tells the action part in each sentence below.

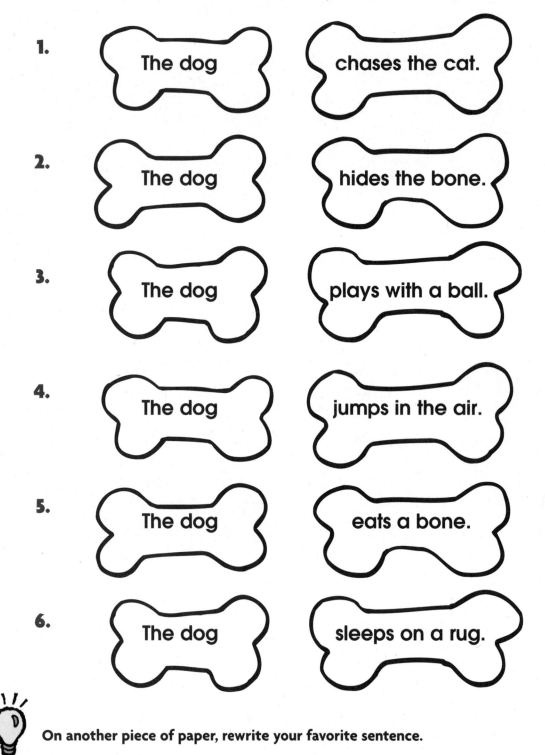

1. The dog   chases the cat.

2. The dog   hides the bone.

3. The dog   plays with a ball.

4. The dog   jumps in the air.

5. The dog   eats a bone.

6. The dog   sleeps on a rug.

On another piece of paper, rewrite your favorite sentence.

Mighty Good Sentences

Choose the ending that tells what each dog is doing. Remember to use periods.

is eating.

is sleeping.

is jumping.

is barking.

1. The white dog _____

_____

2. The gray dog _____

_____

3. The spotted dog _____

_____

4. The striped dog _____

On another piece of paper, draw another dog and write a sentence about it.

A Busy Classroom

*The action part of a sentence is called the **verb**.*

Complete each sentence with an action verb to tell what is happening in the picture. Remember to use periods.

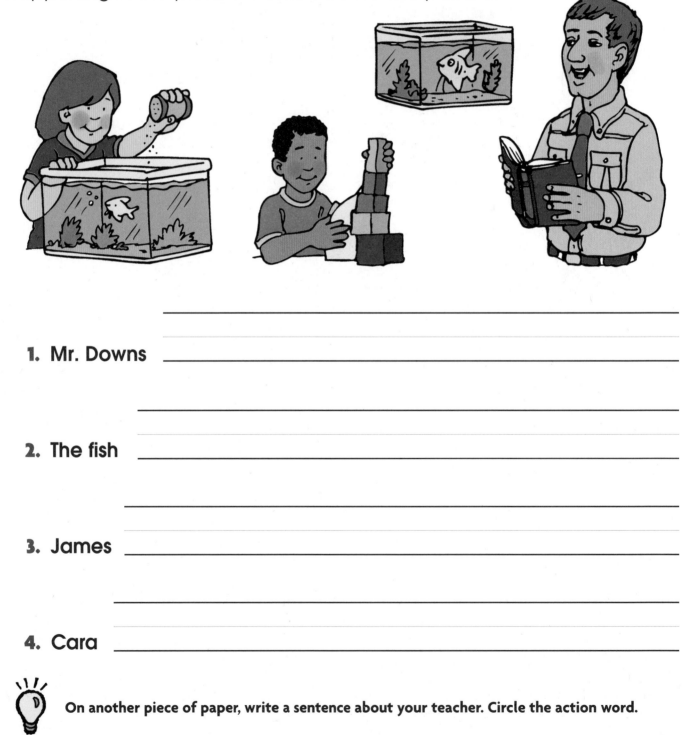

1. Mr. Downs _____

2. The fish _____

3. James _____

4. Cara _____

On another piece of paper, write a sentence about your teacher. Circle the action word.

Pencil It In

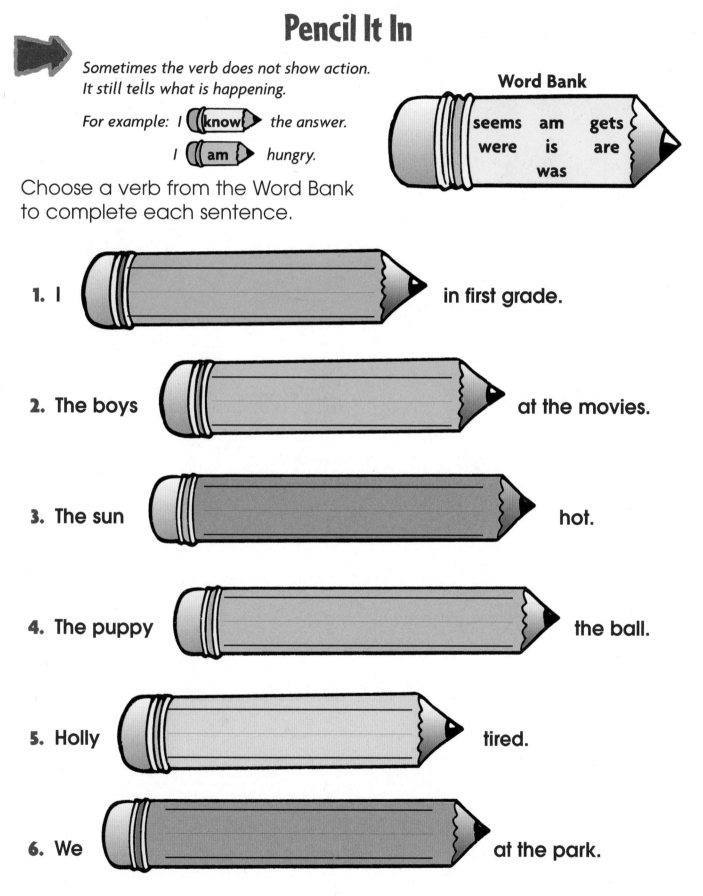

*Sometimes the verb does not show action.
It still tells what is happening.*

For example: I know the answer.

I am hungry.

Choose a verb from the Word Bank
to complete each sentence.

Word Bank

seems   am   gets
were   is   are
was

1. I _____ in first grade.

2. The boys _____ at the movies.

3. The sun _____ hot.

4. The puppy _____ the ball.

5. Holly _____ tired.

6. We _____ at the park.

Topsy-Turvy!

A sentence has a verb that tells what is happening.

Write five silly sentences that tell what is happening in the pictures.

_____

1. _____

_____

2. _____

_____

3. _____

_____

4. _____

_____

5. _____

What Is Going On?

Look around you. Write four sentences that tell what is happening.

1. _____

_____

_____

2. _____

_____

_____

3. _____

_____

_____

4. _____

_____

_____

Find five action words in your favorite book. Write them on another piece of paper.

The Caboose

*A sentence is more interesting when it tells **where** the action is happening.*

In each caboose, draw a picture to show where each sentence takes place.

1.

The plane flew into the clouds.

2.

The princess played in the castle.

3.

The boys fished in the lake.

Chugging Along

Write an ending for each sentence that tells where the action takes place.

naming part	the action	where
1. The monkey	swings	
2. The ball	flew	
3. Jenna's family	went	
4. The pig	slept	
5. The glass	fell	

When Was That?

*A sentence may also tell **when** the action takes place.*

Circle the part that tells when in each sentence.

1. George Washington lived long ago.

2. The mail carrier was late yesterday.

3. The bear slept in winter.

4. We are going to the zoo today.

5. The leaves change in the fall.

6. I lost my tooth last night.

7. It rained all day.

8. The party starts at noon.

9. We got home yesterday.

10. We ate turkey on Thanksgiving Day.

11. The kitten was playing this morning.

12. Tomorrow I am going to my grandmother's house.

On another piece of paper, make a time line of your life. Use it to write two sentences that tell when.

My Busy Day

*Part of a sentence may tell **when** the action happened.*

Write the beginning part of each sentence to tell about your day.
Draw a picture to match each sentence.

_____
_____
_____
_____

this morning.

_____
_____
_____
_____

this afternoon.

_____
_____
_____
_____

tonight.

**On another piece of paper, write four sentences and draw four pictures to tell about your best
day ever.**

Silly Sentences

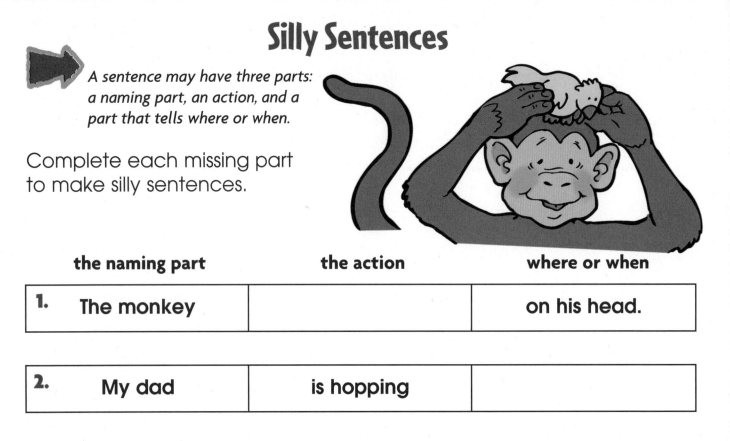

A sentence may have three parts: a naming part, an action, and a part that tells where or when.

Complete each missing part to make silly sentences.

the naming part	the action	where or when
1. The monkey		on his head.
2. My dad	is hopping	
3.	flipped	in the forest.
4. The ball	bounced	
5. My shoes		at the pool.
6. The snake	twisted	
7. The bubbles	filled	

On another piece of paper, write a new sentence by scrambling three parts listed above. For example, use the naming part from #1, the action part from #2, and where or when from #3. Draw a picture of your sentence.

Sweet Sentences

Use choices from each part to make three "sweet" sentences.

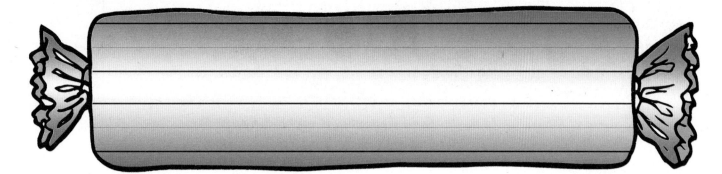

naming part	action	where or when
I	ate doughnuts	at the bakery
She	ate candy	at the party
He	chewed gum	at the circus

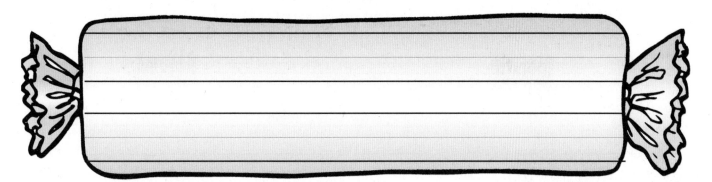

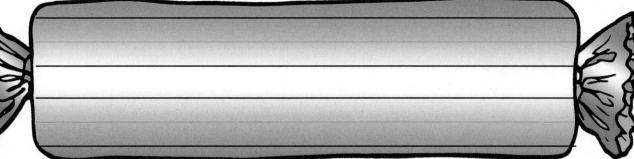

On another piece of paper, name the three parts of this sentence: The doughnut shop closed at noon.

Home Sweet Home

Write three sentences about the picture. For example: The dog is sleeping outside.

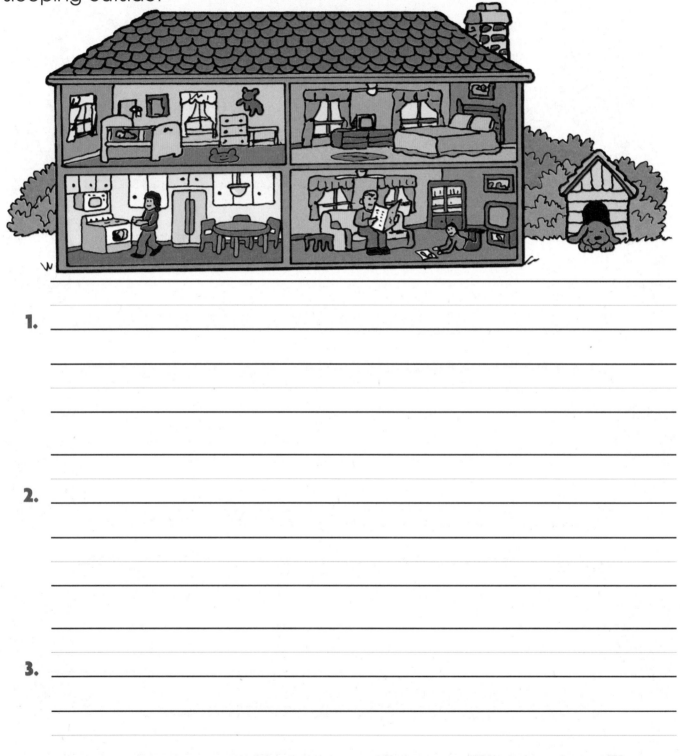

1. _____

   _____

   _____

2. _____

   _____

   _____

3. _____

   _____

   _____

The Construction Crew

Write three sentences about the picture. Include three parts in each sentence.

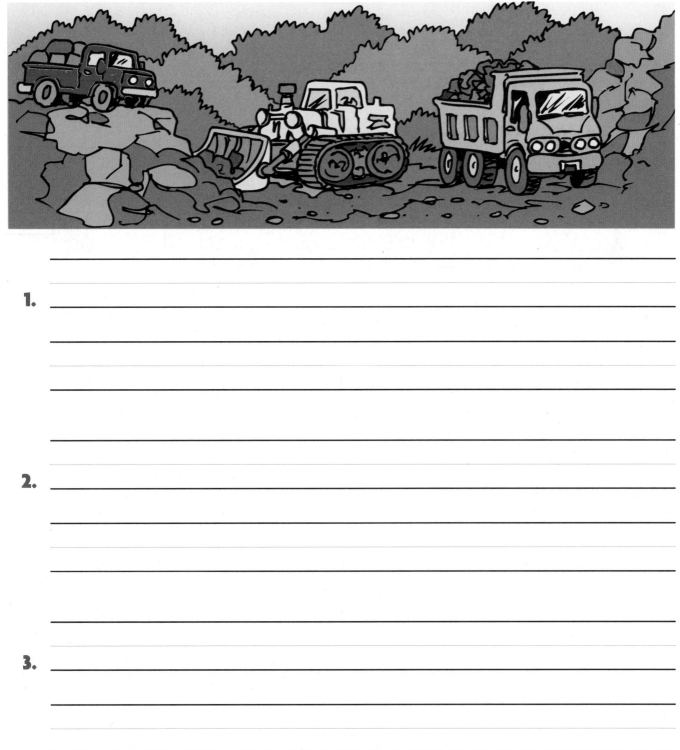

1. _____

_____

_____

2. _____

_____

_____

3. _____

_____

_____

Mystery Boxes

Describing words help you imagine how something looks, feels, smells, sounds, or tastes.

Read the describing words to guess the mystery object. Use the Word Bank to help you.

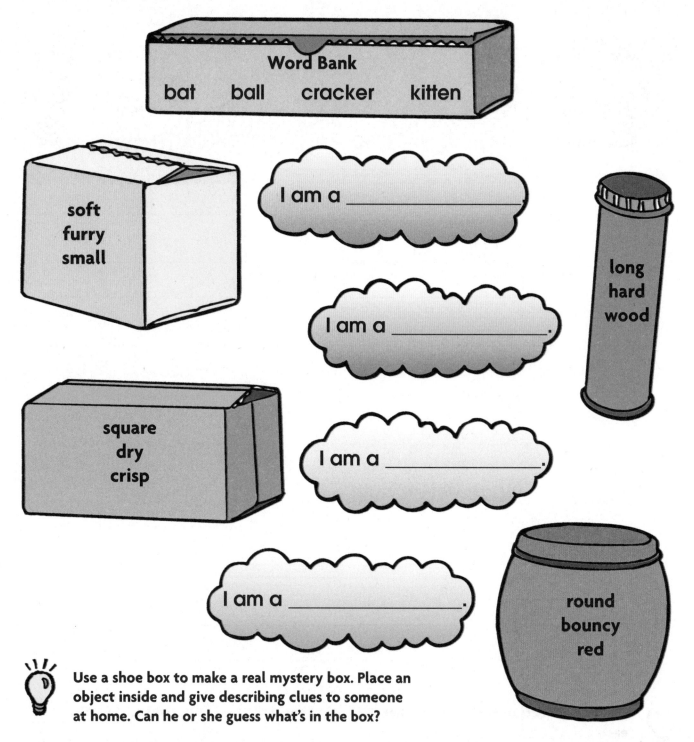

Word Bank

bat   ball   cracker   kitten

soft
furry
small

I am a _____.

I am a _____.

long
hard
wood

square
dry
crisp

I am a _____.

I am a _____.

round
bouncy
red

Use a shoe box to make a real mystery box. Place an object inside and give describing clues to someone at home. Can he or she guess what's in the box?

Sensational Words

Choose words from the Word Bank to describe each picture.

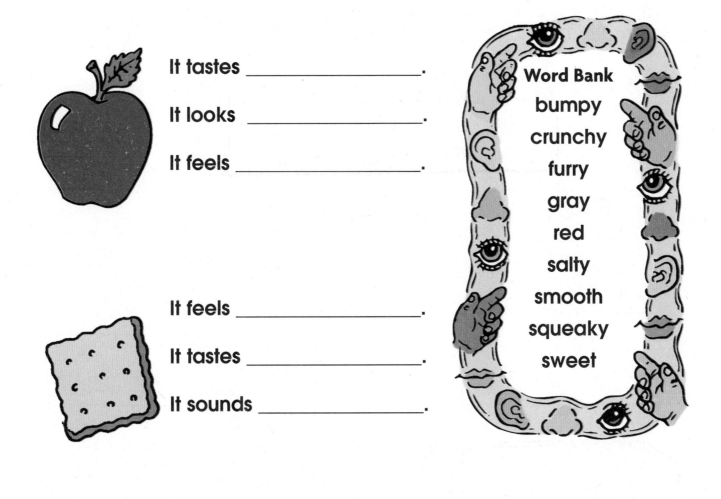

It tastes _____.

It looks _____.

It feels _____.

Word Bank
bumpy
crunchy
furry
gray
red
salty
smooth
squeaky
sweet

It feels _____.

It tastes _____.

It sounds _____.

It looks _____.

It sounds _____.

It feels _____.

Find two objects outside. On another piece of paper, write two adjectives to describe each object.

More Describing Words

How would you describe a lollipop or a baby chick?
Complete the chart below with describing words for each.
Choose words from the Word Bank.

Word Bank

thin	thick	smooth	bumpy	fuzzy
soft	hard	fluffy	shiny	sticky

Lollipop

Chick

_____   _____

_____   _____

_____   _____

_____   _____

1 Name something that is thin. _____

2 Name something that is thick. _____

3 Name something that is bumpy. _____

Pretty Packages

The describing words in a sentence help the reader paint a picture in his or her mind.

Write three words to describe each gift. Then color them to match.

_____ (color)

_____ (color)

_____ (pattern)

_____ (color)

_____ (color)

_____ (pattern)

_____ (color)

_____ (color)

_____ (pattern)

_____ (color)

_____ (color)

_____ (pattern)

Describe a "mystery object" to a friend. Can he or she guess what you are describing?

What's Inside?

Use describing words to write a sentence about each package.
For example: I found a swimsuit in the **yellow square** box.

1. I found _____ in the

_____

_____ package.

2. I found _____ in the

_____

_____ package.

3. I found _____ in the

_____

_____ package.

4. I found _____ in the

_____

_____ package.

A Walk in the Park

Describing words make a sentence more interesting.

Write describing words to finish each sentence.

1. A _____ duck is

swimming in the _____ pond.

2. A _____ man is walking

his _____ dog.

3. A _____ girl is

flying a _____ kite.

4. A _____ woman is sitting

on a _____ .

On another piece of paper, draw a picture of your favorite animal at the zoo. Then write two words to describe this animal.

Around Town

Write a sentence for each picture. Use the describing word in the sentence.

large

beautiful

crowded

noisy

On another piece of paper, write five words that describe your street.

Keep It in Order

Sentences can be written in order to tell a story.

Finish each story by writing sentences about the last pictures.

1. First, the spider crawls up.

Next, _____

Last, _____

2. First, there is a tadpole

Next, _____

Last, _____

What's Next?

Sentences can be written in order to give directions.

Finish each set of directions by writing sentences about the last pictures.

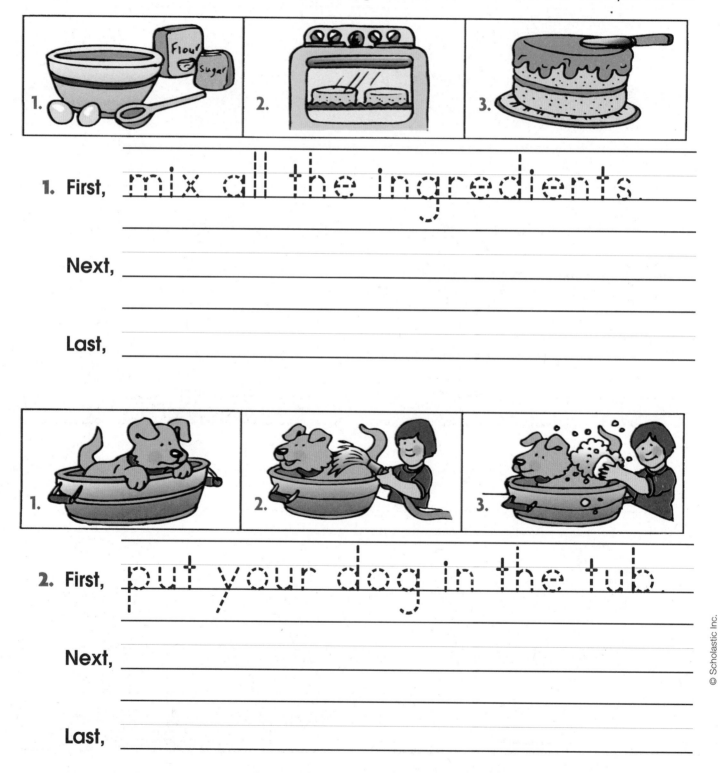

1. First, mix all the ingredients.

Next,

Last,

2. First, put your dog in the tub.

Next,

Last,

Which Title Fits?

 *The name of a story is called the **title**. It matches with the story. Most of the words in a title begin with capital letters.*

Match each title with its story. Write the title above the picture.

A Big Beak	**The Big Win**
My Space Friend	**A Knight's Tale**

_____
(title)

_____
(title)

_____
(title)

_____
(title)

© Scholastic Inc.

A Terrific Title

Fill in the missing words to make your own story. Then write a title that fits with your story. Draw a picture about your story in the box.

_____

(title)

One _____ **day,**

_____ **took his pet**

_____ **for a walk. First,**

they went to the _____.

Then they walked to _____'s

house. Last, they went home to _____

_____. **It was a**

_____ **day!**

© Scholastic Inc.

Story Strips

 A story has a beginning, middle, and end.

Write a sentence to tell about each part of the story. Remember to
give the story a title.

Beginning

(title)

Middle

End

More Story Strips

A story has a beginning, middle, and end.

Think of a story you know well. Write about the beginning, middle, and end parts. Draw pictures to match. Be sure to give your story a title.

_____

(title)

Beginning

Middle

End

Fold a piece of paper two times to make a storybook. Write a story and draw pictures to match. Do not forget to write a title for your story.

Places in Pictures

Pretend you are on
cloud in the sky.
You look down.
You take a photo.
Here it is!

Circle **YES** if you see the thing in the photo.
Circle **NO** if you do not.

1. house   YES   NO

2. street   YES   NO

3. tree   YES   NO

4. pond   YES   NO

5. **What else do you see?** _____

You can show a place on a map.
A map is a drawing of a place from above.
This map shows the same place that the photo does.

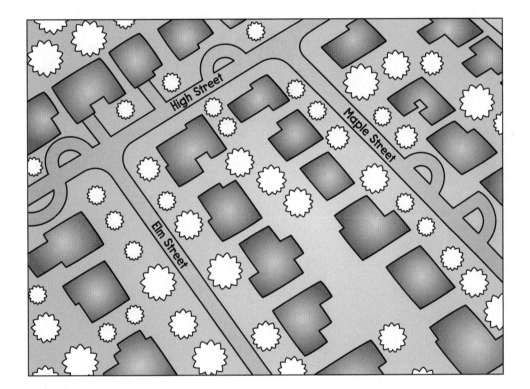

6. **Find a street on the photo.**
   Then find the same street on the map.
   Write the name of the street. _____

7. **The trees on the map are not colored.**
   Color them green.

8. **Find a swimming pool in the photo.**
   Draw it in the same place on the map.

Making a Map

This picture shows a toy store.

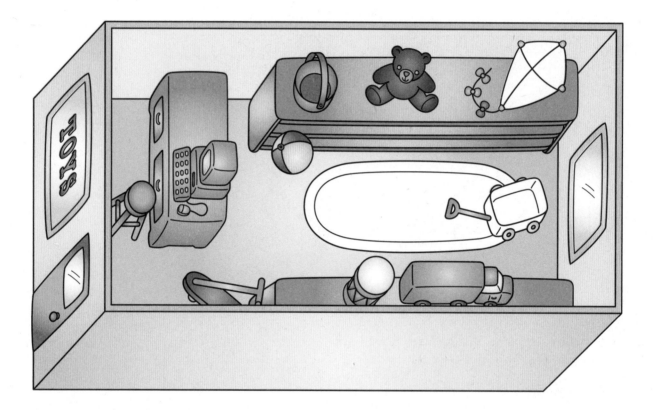

1. Color the kite yellow.

2. Color the rug green.

3. Color the wagon red.

4. What is next to the drum? _____

5. Can you buy a teddy bear here? _____

This map shows the same toy store.
You can help draw the map.

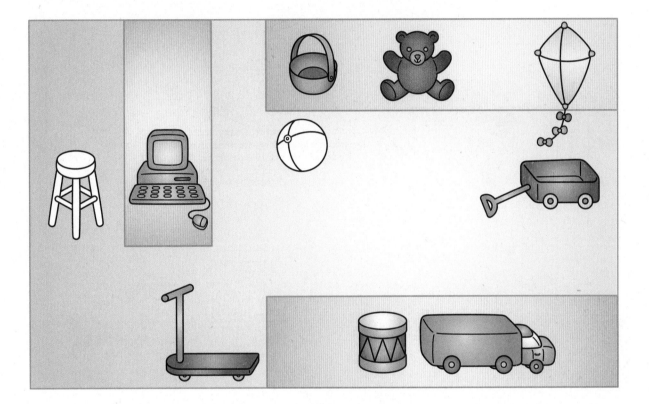

6. Find the ball in the picture.
   Make it the same color on the map.

7. Find the stool in the picture.
   Make it the same color on the map.

8. Find the rug in the picture.
   Draw it on the map in the same place.

Map Words

Many map words tell where things are.

The bird is **near** the branch.

The bird is **far** from the branch.

The bird is to the **left** of the bird house.

The bird is to the **right** of the bird house.

The bird is **above** the bath.

The bird is **below** the bath.

Write a word to complete each sentence.

near   far   left   right   above

1. The bird is _____ from the bird house.

2. The girl is _____ the bird house.

3. The bird is _____ the grass.

4. The bird house is to the _____ of the girl.

5. The path is to the _____ of the girl.

Big and Small Spaces

Maps can show big spaces or small spaces.

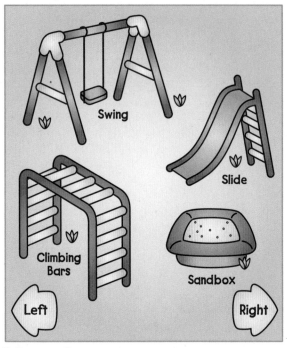

Map 1: This map shows a school playground.

Map 2: This map shows all of the school grounds.

Circle **YES** if the sentence is true.
Circle **NO** if the sentence is not true.

1. **The school is bigger than the trees.**   YES NO

2. **The playground is bigger than the parking lot.** YES NO

3. **The school is to the right of the playground.**   YES NO

4. **The trees are to the right of the playground.**   YES NO

Map 3: This map shows three streets. Can you find the school?

5. **What is the biggest building on this map?** _____

6. **What is the smallest building on this map?** _____

7. **Look at all three maps. Which map shows the biggest space?** _____

8. **Which map shows the smallest space?** _____

Looking at Earth

**If you were in outer space, you could see Earth.
It would look like this.**

1. **What shape is Earth?** _____

2. **Who lives on Earth?** _____

3. **Draw something
   that is the same shape
   as Earth.**

A Globe

A globe is a model of Earth.
It is the same shape as Earth.

1. **What colors do you see on the globe?**

   _____

2. **What color stands for water?**

   _____

3. **Is a globe smaller or bigger than Earth?**

   _____

Directions

Earth has four main directions.
They are north, south, east, and west.

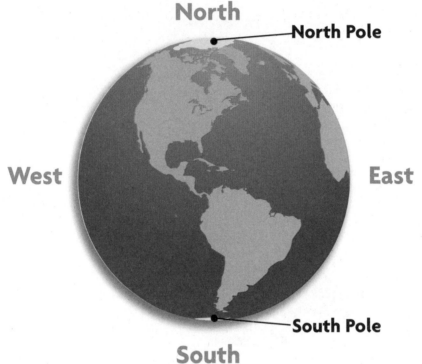

North is the direction toward the North Pole.
South is the direction toward the South Pole.

Can you find east and west on the picture, too?

1. What direction is the opposite of north? _____

2. What direction is the opposite of west? _____

Directions help you find places on a map.
This map shows a camp.
Point to the four directions.

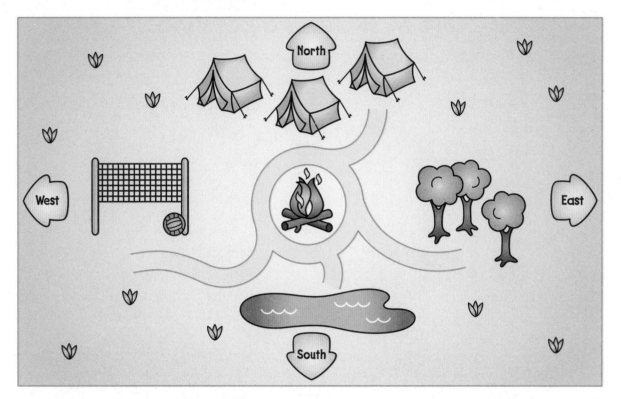

Where is each thing?
Write a direction word to describe it.

1. _____

2. _____

3. _____

4. _____

Using Directions

Directions tell you which way to go.
This map shows a pet shop.

Write the direction word that tells how to get there.

1. from 🐦 to 🐱

2. from 🐟 to 🐰

3. from 🐕 to 🏪

4. from 🏪 to 🥫

Come to the fair! You can have fun.

Draw a line to show where you go.

1. **Start at the gate. Go north to the** **. Mmmm!**

2. **Now go west. Stop and ride on the** .

3. **Walk to the east. Get your face painted like a** .

4. **From here, go west and then north. Stop and play at the** .

5. **In which direction is the gate from the**  **?**

Symbols

A symbol is a drawing that stands for something real.

The photo shows a road.

This is a symbol for a road.

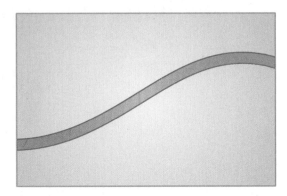

Draw a line to match each photo to the correct symbol.

1.

2.

3.

4.

a.

b.

c.

d.

Here are some more symbols.

Draw the correct symbol next to each photo.

1.

3.

2.

4.

Symbols on Maps

Most maps have symbols.
A map key tells what each symbol stands for.

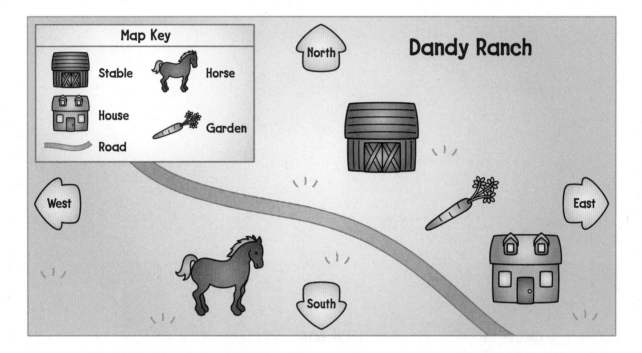

Use the map key.
Write what each symbol stands for.

1.

2.

3.

4.

The ranch has one new animal.

Circle the new animal on the map.
Use the map key to answer the questions.

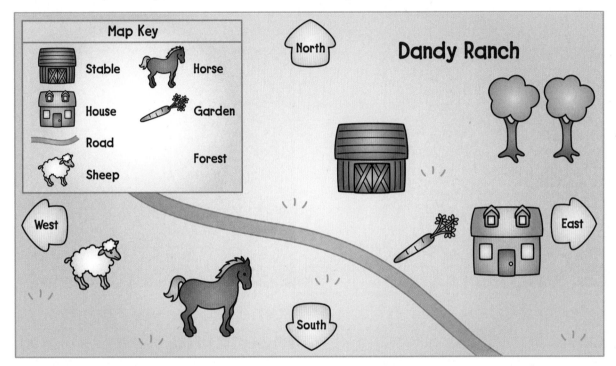

1. Is the horse north or south of the road? _____

2. What does 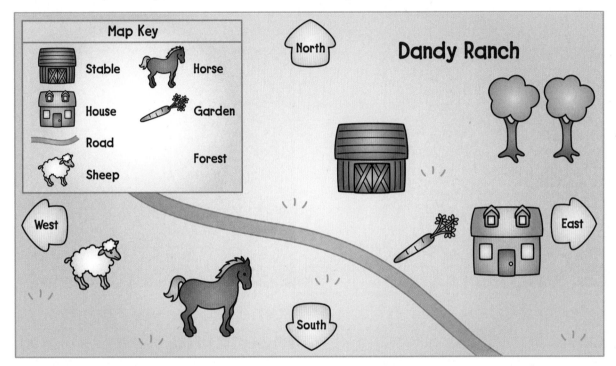 mean? _____

3. Is the garden east or west of the house? _____

4. Find the forest on the map.
   Add a tree symbol to the map key.

Land and Water

Earth has different kinds of land.

Some land is flat.
A **plain** is flat land.

Some land is very high. A
mountain is very high land.

Some land is higher than
a plain but not as high as
a mountain. This land is
called a **hill**.

1. What is the highest kind of land?

_____

2. What is the flattest land?

_____

3. Which is higher, a hill or a plain?

_____

Earth has lots of water.

Some water runs across the land. This water is called a **river.**

Some water has land all around it. This water is called a **lake**.

These symbols stand for different kinds of land and water. Write a word to tell what each symbol stands for.

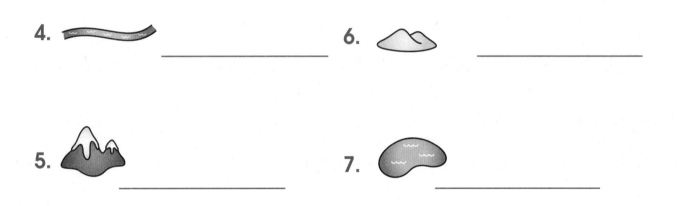

4. _____

6. _____

5. _____

7. _____

A Land and Water Map

This picture shows different kinds of land and water.

1. Find the river. Color it blue.

2. Find a body of water with land all around it.
   Write "lake" on it.

3. Find the hills. Color them light green.

4. Find the flat land. Write "plain" on it.

This map shows land and water, too.

1. What does mean? _____

2. Is the lake to the east or west of the river? _____

3. Are the mountains to the
   east or west of the hills? _____

4. Write a place where you can do each thing.

   climb _____   run _____

   swim _____   fish _____

A Park Map

This map shows a big park.
A park can have different kinds of land and water.

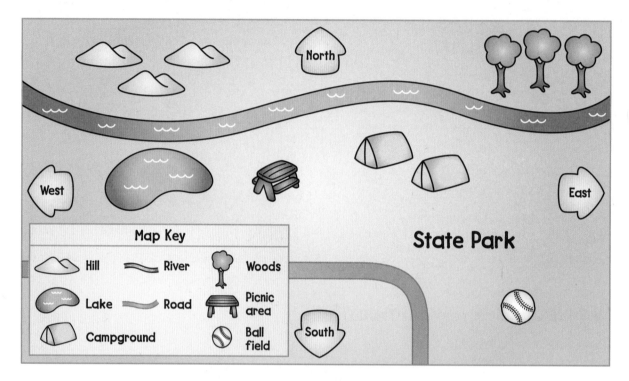

1. What does this symbol ⛰ mean? _____

2. Where can you sleep in this park? _____

3. What symbol shows where
   you can have a picnic? _____

4. Where can you ride a raft in this park? _____

5. Is the road to the east
   or west of the ball field? _____

This map shows a city park.

Map Key

Doony Park — Entrance

Dog run

Playground

Bench

Flagpole

Path

Snack stand

Fountain

Doony Park

North

West

East

South

1. What is the name of this park?

   _____

2. Where can you get something to eat?

   _____

3. What is north of the entrance?

   _____

4. Where can your dog
   play in this park?

   _____

5. Where can you ride a swing?

   _____

6. In which direction
   would you walk from the 🟦 to the ☂ _____

A Neighborhood Map

A map can show a neighborhood.

A neighborhood is a place where people live, work, and play. The people who live in a neighborhood are neighbors.

These pictures show different parts of Dale's neighborhood. Write a word for each picture.

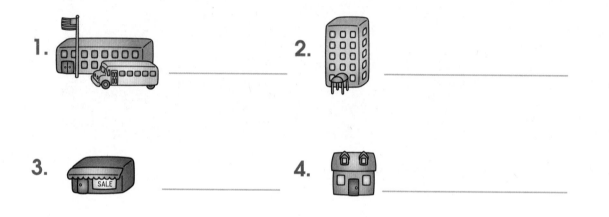

1. _____

2. _____

3. _____

4. _____

5. **Draw a picture of something in your neighborhood.**

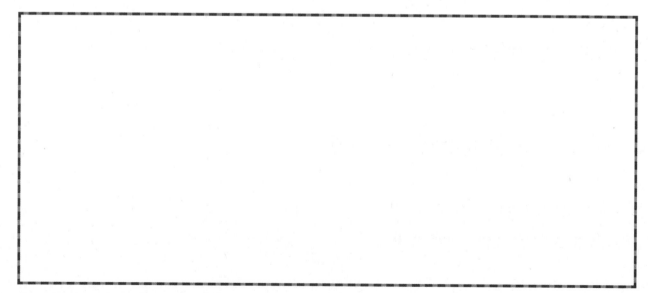

This map shows the neighborhood where Dale lives.

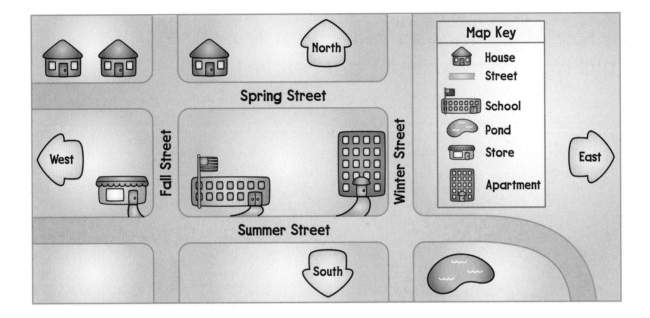

1. What does the symbol

    stand for? _____

2. Find the symbol for house.
   On what street are the houses? _____

3. Dale lives in an apartment.
   On what street does Dale live? _____

4. Dale is going to the store
   with her father. In which direction
   is the store from her home? _____

Going Places

Hari's family just moved to Wonder Town.
Use this map to help them get around.

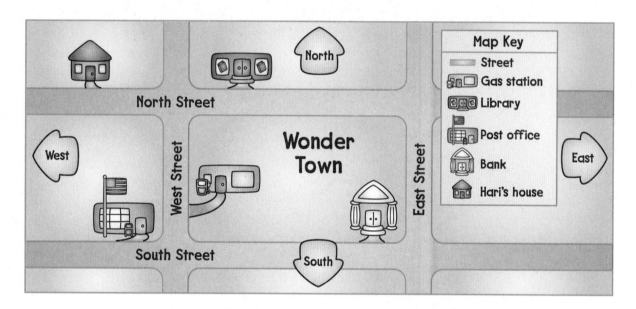

Tell Hari's family the street for each place.

1. **Hari's mother is going
   to the bank. It is on** _____ .

2. **Hari's father is going
   to the gas station. It is on** _____ .

3. **Hari's big brother is going
   to the library. It is on** _____ .

4. **Hari's grandma is going
   to the post office. It is on** _____ .

Hari goes to school the same way each day. He follows a route. A route is a way to go from one place to another.

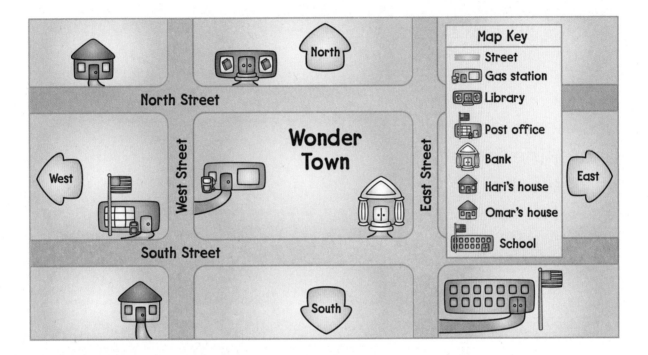

1. **Start at Hari's house.**
   Draw a line to show the route he can take to school.

2. **On what street is the school?** _____

3. **Omar is Hari's new friend.**
   Draw a line to show Omar's route to school.

4. **Does Omar live east or**
   west of the school? _____

5. **Is the library north or**
   south of the gas station? _____

Borders

**Maps show where places begin and end.
A dividing line between two places is called a border.**

Look at the fence in this photo. The fence shows where the border is.

Look at the line with dashes on this map. This line is a symbol. It stands for a border.

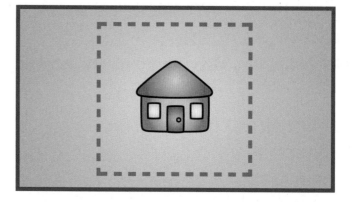

Maps show other kinds of borders, too. A river can be a border. So can a road. Draw an X on three kinds of borders on this map.

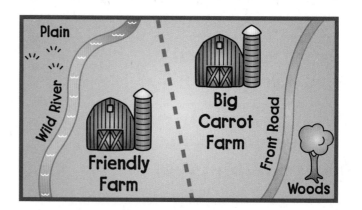

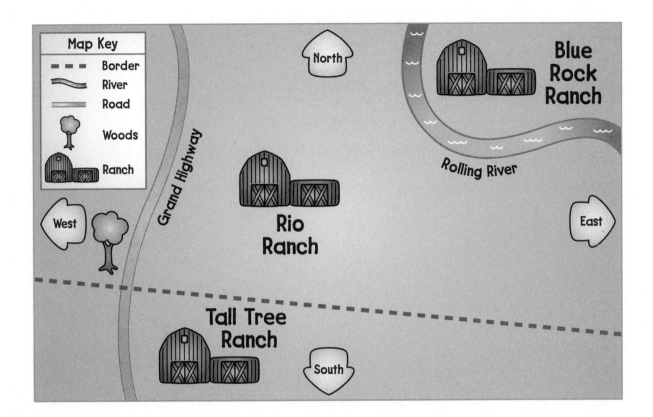

This map shows different borders.

1. This symbol   - - - - -   stands for a _____.

2. The border to the west of
   Rio Ranch is a _____.

3. What is the border between
   Rio Ranch and Blue Rock Ranch?_____

4. In which direction is Tall Tree Ranch
   from Rio Ranch?_____

5. Are the woods east or
   west of Rio Ranch? _____

The United States

Here is a map of the United States.

The United States is a large **country**.
A country is a land and people who live there.

The United States has 50 states.
Each state is a part of the country.
The states are different shapes and sizes.

MAINE
VERMONT
NEW HAMPSHIRE
MASSACHUSETTS
NEW YORK
RHODE ISLAND
CONNECTICUT
PENNSYLVANIA
NEW JERSEY
DELAWARE
WEST VIRGINIA
MARYLAND
VIRGINIA
WASHINGTON, D.C.
NORTH CAROLINA
SOUTH CAROLINA
East
FLORIDA

MAP KEY

—— State border
✪ National capital

1. What does this symbol ——— mean?

_____

2. What is your state?

_____

3. How many states share a border with your state?

_____

4. Name a state in the east.

_____

5. Is Texas in the north or south?

_____

6. Is Oregon in the west or east?

_____

7. What state is south of Utah?

_____

8. What state is west of Ohio?

_____

A State Map

This map shows the state of Indiana. Each state has a capital city.

A capital is the city where the leaders of the state work. The capital of Indiana is Indianapolis.

1. What does this symbol ★ stand for?

   _____

2. Is Evansville in the north or south of the state?_____

3. In what part of the state is South Bend?_____

4. Is Riverview in the west or the east part of the state?_____

This map shows where Indiana is in the United States.

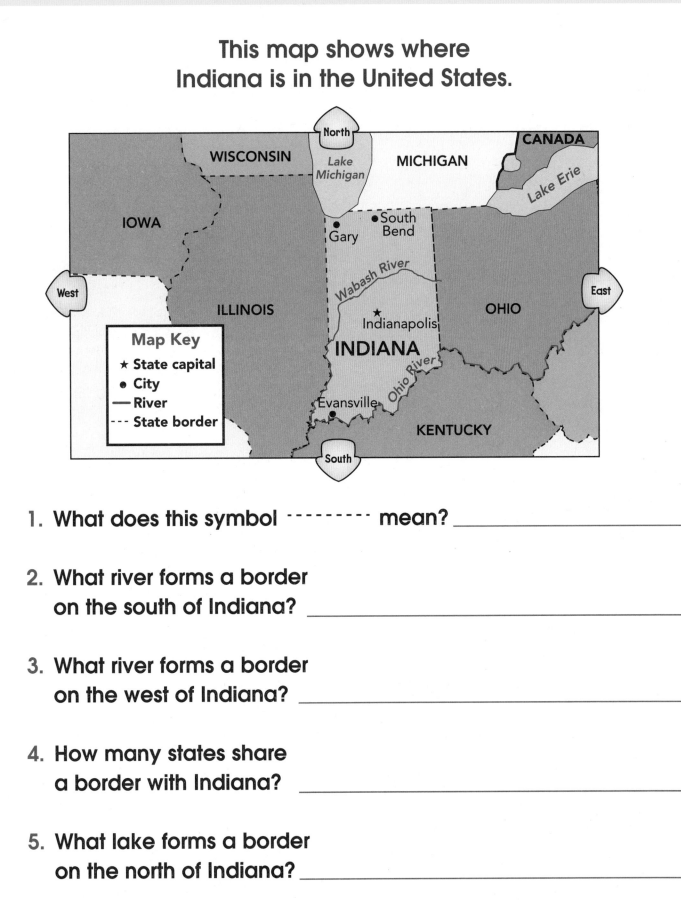

1. What does this symbol - - - - - - - - mean? _____

2. What river forms a border on the south of Indiana? _____

3. What river forms a border on the west of Indiana? _____

4. How many states share a border with Indiana? _____

5. What lake forms a border on the north of Indiana? _____

A City Map

The United States has a capital city.

It is Washington, D.C.
The President of the
United States lives and
works there. So do other
leaders of the country.

The President lives and
works in the White House.

Washington, D.C., has many important buildings.
You can see some of them on the map on the next page.

1. **Find the Washington Monument.**
   Is it north or south of the White House? _____

2. **Find the U.S. Capitol.**
   Trace a route on the map to the White House.

3. **Find the National Gallery of Art.**
   Is it east or west of the U.S. Capitol? _____

4. **Constitution Avenue runs from west to** _____ .

5. **Name a museum you would like to visit.**

   _____

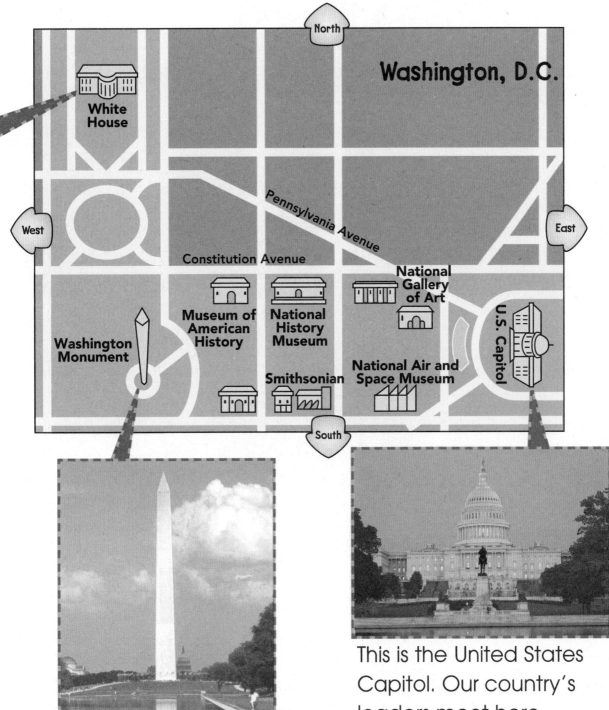

Washington, D.C.

North

West

East

South

Pennsylvania Avenue

Constitution Avenue

White House

National Gallery of Art

Museum of American History

National History Museum

U.S. Capitol

Washington Monument

Smithsonian

National Air and Space Museum

This is the Washington Monument. It honors George Washington. He was our first President.

This is the United States Capitol. Our country's leaders meet here.

North America

This map shows North America. North America is a continent.

A continent is a large body of land.
The United States is in North America.

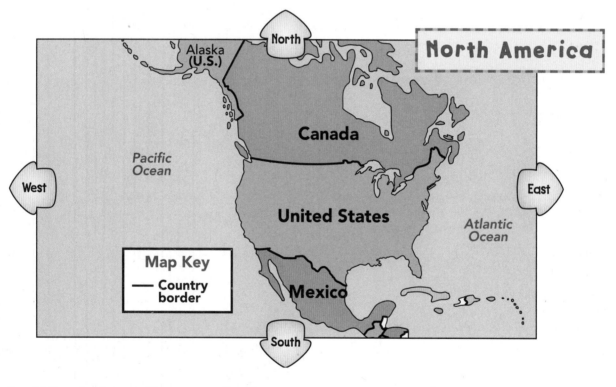

1. What does the symbol ———— mean?_____

2. What country is north
   of the United States? _____

3. In which direction is Mexico
   from the United States? _____

Around the continents are Earth's oceans.
An ocean is a very big body of salt water.

Earth has five oceans.
This map shows two of them.

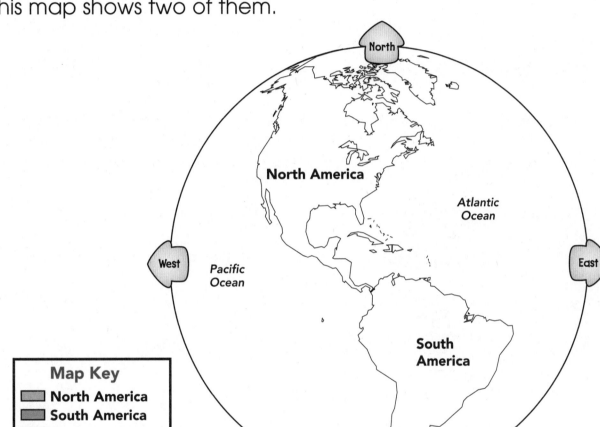

Map Key
- North America
- South America
- Ocean

1. What ocean is to the
   east of North America? _____

2. What ocean is to the
   west of North America? _____

3. Color the map to match the map key.

A World Map

Remember, Earth is round like a ball. But you can only see one side of a ball at once.

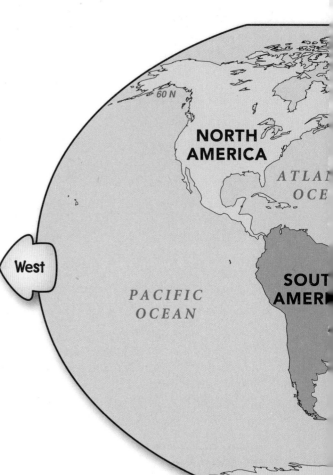

1. Here is a map of Earth. It shows all of Earth's continents. Count to find seven continents.

2. The map shows the five oceans of Earth, too. What are their names? _____

   _____   _____

   _____   _____

3. Which continent is north of Africa? _____

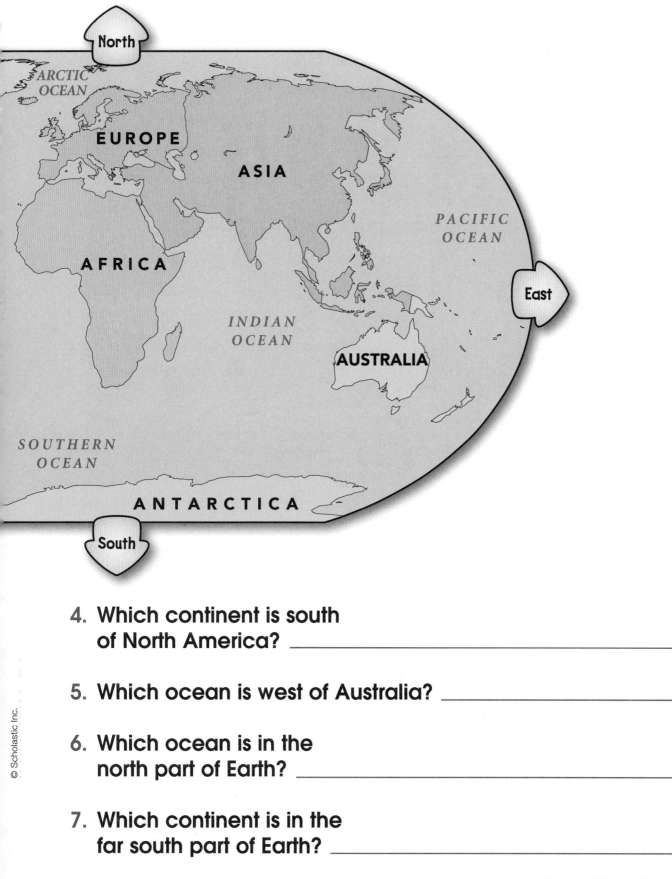

4. Which continent is south of North America? _____

5. Which ocean is west of Australia? _____

6. Which ocean is in the north part of Earth? _____

7. Which continent is in the far south part of Earth? _____

Map Review 1

Use the map to answer the questions.

Map Key
- Street
- Gas station
- Library
- Post office
- Bank
- Hari's house
- Omar's house
- School
- Pond
- Hill

North Street

Wonder Town

West Street

East Street

West

East

South Street

North

South

1. What does this symbol ⬭ mean? _____

2. What kind of land is to the east of the bank? _____

3. On what street does Hari live? _____

4. Draw a route from Hari's house to Omar's house.

5. Where can Hari mail a letter? _____

6. Is Hari's house north or south of the school? _____

Map Review 2

Use the map to answer the questions.

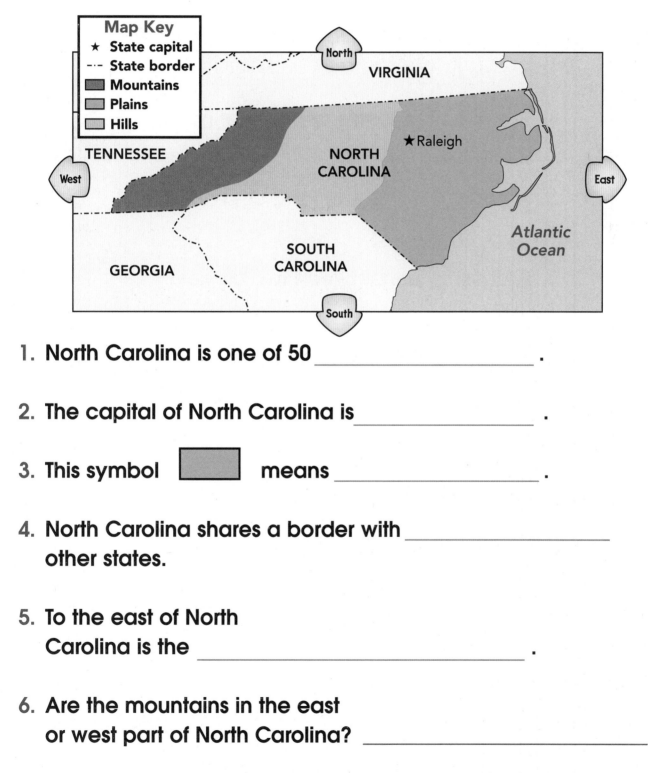

1. North Carolina is one of 50 _____ .

2. The capital of North Carolina is _____ .

3. This symbol [   ] means _____ .

4. North Carolina shares a border with _____ other states.

5. To the east of North Carolina is the _____ .

6. Are the mountains in the east or west part of North Carolina? _____

Thinking About Maps

You have learned a lot about maps. Use what you know to find the secret words.

1. The direction that is opposite of north.

___ ___
7   4

2. A body of water with land all around it.

___ ___ ___
   9   5

3. A dividing line between two places.

___ ___ ___ ___ ___
        6

4. A drawing that stands for something real.

___ ___ ___
12

5. Very high land.

___ ___ ___ ___ ___
   1   8   3 2

6. A way to go from one place to another.

___ ___ ___ ___
     10 11

Now, can you figure out the secret words?

___ ___ ___ ___ ___ ___ ___ ___ ___ ___ ___ ___
1 2 3 4 5 6 7 8 9 10 11 12

Glossary

border   A border is a dividing line between two places.

capital   A capital is a city where government leaders work.

continent   A continent is a large body of land. North America is a continent.

country   A country is a land where people live.

direction   A direction tells where something is. The four main directions are north, south, east, and west.

east   East is one of the four main directions. East is the opposite of west.

Earth   Earth is the planet on which people live.

far   Far is a word that tells where things are. Far is the opposite of near.

globe   A globe is a model of Earth.

hill   A hill is land that is higher than a plain but not as high as a mountain.

lake   A lake is a body of water that has land all around it.

left   Left is a word that tells where things are. Left is the opposite of right.

map   A map is a drawing of a place from above. A map shows part or all of Earth.

map key	A map key is a list of symbols used on a map. The map key tells what each symbol means.
mountain	A mountain is very high land.
near	Near is a word that tells where things are. Near is the opposite of far.
neighborhood	A neighborhood is a place where people live and work.
north	North is one of the four main directions. North is the direction toward the North Pole.
ocean	An ocean is a very large body of water. Earth has five oceans.
plain	A plain is flat land.
right	Right is a word that tells where things are. Right is the opposite of left.
river	A river is a body of water that flows across the land.
route	A route is a way to go from one place to another.
south	South is one of the four main directions. South is the direction toward the South Pole.
state	A state is part of the United States. There are 50 states.
symbol	A symbol is a drawing that stands for something real.
west	West is one of the four main directions. West is the opposite of east.

© Scholastic Inc.

Beautiful Babies

Cross out every other letter to name the baby animal.
Write the name on the line. The first one has been done for you.

1. ___kitten___

2. _____

3. _____

4. _____

5. _____

6. _____

7. _____

8. _____

9. _____

10. _____

A baby elephant has the same name as a baby cow. What is it? _____

Babies Change and Grow!

**Read about animal babies.
Then try the science investigations.**

Emperor Penguin

A baby penguin is called a **chick**. Its head is black and white. Its body is covered in fluffy gray feathers called **down**. As the chick grows, its head turns black. It grows new feathers on its body—black for its back and white for its belly!

Silver Leaf Monkey

This baby monkey has bright orange fur. That helps the adults see it in the dark forest. As it grows older, the monkey's fur will change color. It will turn dark gray—just like its parents' fur.

Warty Newt

This is a newt. It lives in a pond. A newt starts out as an egg in the water. When it hatches, it becomes a **larva**. The larva breathes underwater with **gills**, just like a fish. But a newt's gills are on top of its head! When the larva turns into an adult, it lives on land.

larva

adult

Investigation 1

An emperor penguin does not leave its egg in a nest. It carries its egg on its feet! What is it like to walk with an egg on your feet? Try it!

© Scholastic Inc.

1. Gather the materials you will need.

2. Pour the rice into the zip-top bag. Press out the air. Seal the bag and roll it up. Put it inside a sock. Tuck in the top of the sock. This is your penguin egg.

3. A penguin father carries his egg on his feet. Put your egg on top of your feet. Carefully walk around the room. If the egg falls off your feet, stop. Pick it up and put it back on your feet.

4. What did you do to make sure the egg stayed on your feet? (Did you turn your feet a new way? Speed up or slow down? What else?) Record on the next page.

5. **Think:** Why do you think penguin fathers carry their eggs on their feet? How do they keep the eggs safe?

Materials

★ 1 cup rice

★ quart-sized zip-top plastic bag

★ sock

★ recording sheet (next page)

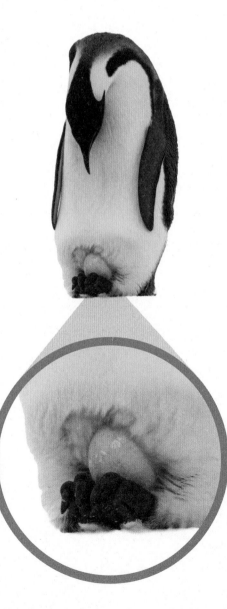

1. Do Steps 2 and 3 of the investigation. What happened?

_____

_____

_____

2. What did you do to make sure the egg stayed on your feet?

_____

_____

_____

3. Why do you think penguin fathers carry their eggs on their feet? How do they keep the eggs safe?

_____

_____

_____

Investigation 2

Some baby animals have bright colors so their parents can find them easily. How can you make a baby bird stand out in its habitat (the nature around it)?

Materials

★ crayons

★ recording sheet (next page)

1. Gather your materials.

2. Look at the "pretend" habitat below. Look at the picture of the baby birds on the next page. Imagine they will live in that habitat. Will the white birds stand out or blend in?

3. Color Bird 1 so that it will stand out in the habitat.
Remember: You want your bird to be seen when it's in its habitat.

4. What if you don't want the baby to stand out? What if you want to hide it from enemies? Many baby animals have colors and patterns that make them hard to see. They blend in with their habitats. The name for this kind of blending in is **camouflage**. Color Bird 2 with camouflage.

© Scholastic Inc.

1. Look at the pictures of the baby birds below. Imagine they live in the habitat on the previous page. Do the white birds stand out or blend in?

_____

2. Do Step 3 of the investigation. Is your baby bird easy or hard to see?

_____

3. Do Step 4 of the investigation. How did you **camouflage** (blend in) your baby bird?

_____

Bird 1   **Bird 2**

All Kinds of Animals

Read each clue. Write the names of the correct animals in the crossword puzzle.

Across

2. This mammal hibernates in the winter.

5. This reptile has a long nose and sharp teeth.

6. This mammal makes an oink sound.

7. This mammal has a mane.

Down

1. This bird uses its wings to swim.

3. This mammal lives like a fish.

4. This sea creature has eight arms.

 On another sheet of paper, draw a picture of your favorite animal. Write one sentence about it.

© Scholastic Inc.

A Home for Koalas

Read about koala habitats. Then try the science investigations.

Koalas live in Australia. But people are taking over their habitats, the places where they live. Now there's less food and shelter for the animals.

Koalas are very picky eaters. They eat only the leaves of eucalyptus (yoo-kuh-LIP-tiss) trees. People have cut down many eucalyptus forests. They have turned the land into farms, highways, malls, and houses. Today, there are not many koalas left.

Scientists and other people are now working together to help. They are planting new eucalyptus trees for the koalas. They hope this will help the animals thrive.

Investigation 1

What lives in your community park? Find out!

1. Gather your materials.

2. Close your eyes and imagine you are walking around your community park. What different ways do people use it? Record your thoughts on the next page.

Materials
★ clipboard
★ pencil
★ recording sheet (next page)

3. What other living things do you think might use your community park? They might be living there, or they might just visit. Make a list.

4. Go on a Community Park Safari. Look for signs of life. You can look for living things, like a tree or a butterfly. (Don't touch or disturb anything!) You can also look for clues that something was there. Maybe you will see a nibbled leaf, a spider web, or an animal track. Look carefully at what you find.

5. On your recording sheet, draw two things you found.

6. Share your discoveries with a friend. What surprised you the most?

1. What different ways do people use your community park?

_____

_____

2. What other living things do you think might use your community park?

_____

_____

3. What signs of life did you find on your Community Park Safari? Draw two things you found.

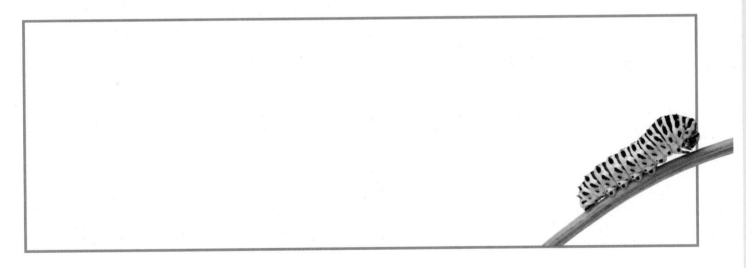

4. What surprised you the most?

_____

Investigation 2

What would you like to live in your community park? How would you change your park to make it a good home?

Materials	

Materials
- ★ pencil
- ★ recording sheet (next page)

1. List three animals or plants you would like to have in your community park.

2. Look at your list. Does your community park have what each one needs to survive? (For clues, use the chart below.)

3. Pick one living thing that could not get what it needs from your community park. How could you change your community park so it would be a good habitat for your plant or animal? Write your ideas on your recording sheet. Draw a picture of the changes.

What Do Living Things Need?

Each kind of living thing has its own special needs. Here are some to think about.	
Food	Some animals eat plants. Some eat other animals.
Water	Some animals just need water to drink. Some plants need to soak up water with their roots. But other plants and animals live in the water, so they need a lot more.
Shelter	An animal might need a cave or a good place to dig an underground burrow. It might need a branch and twigs for making a nest.
Territory	Some animals never travel very far. Some hunt over large areas. Others fly or swim thousands of miles every year.
Temperature	Some plants and animals need warmth. Some are happy in the cold.
Amount of light	Some plants need a lot of sun. Some grow well in the shade.

© Scholastic Inc.

1. List three animals or plants you would like to have in your community park.

_____

_____

2. Do Step 3 of the investigation. Write your ideas below.

_____

_____

3. Draw a picture of one or more of the changes below.

Inspect the Insects

Use the words in the box to identify the parts of an insect.

| leg | antenna | wing | head | abdomen | thorax |

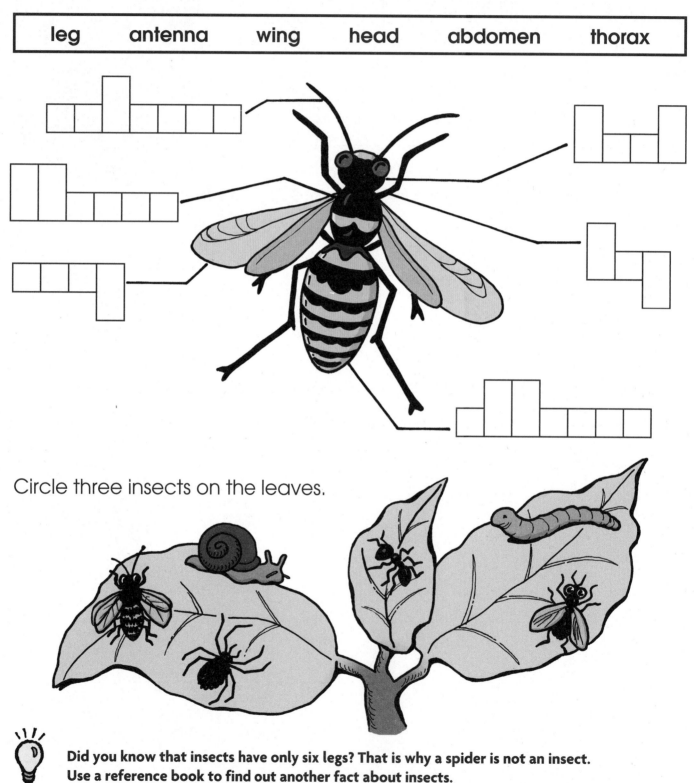

Circle three insects on the leaves.

Did you know that insects have only six legs? That is why a spider is not an insect. Use a reference book to find out another fact about insects.

Way to 'Bee' Helpful!

Read about bees.
Then try the science investigations.

1. A honeybee visits a flower to drink its nectar. Later, the bee will use the nectar to make honey.

2. The bee also gathers tiny grains called pollen. It takes the pollen back to the hive for food. Some extra pollen sticks to the bee's body.

3. The bee flies to a new flower.

4. Some of the extra pollen rubs off the bee's body. The pollen sticks to the new flower.

5. The pollen goes into the flower. It helps form seeds. A fruit grows around the seeds. Someday a hungry animal might eat the fruit. The seeds might drop to the ground and grow into new plants!

Investigation 1

How do bees pollinate flowers? Find out here!

1. Gather the materials you will need.

2. Make a paper-cup flower: Put 1 teaspoon of colored glitter in a small paper cup. The glitter is the flower's pollen. Make 3 more flowers. Use different colors of glitter.

3. Make a pipe-cleaner bee as shown in the diagram below: wrap a yellow then a black pipe-cleaner around a pencil.

Materials

★ 4 tsps glitter (different colors)

★ 4 small paper cups

★ yellow and black pipe-cleaners

★ pencil

★ recording sheet (next page)

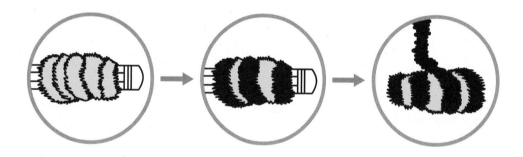

4. Fly your bee into a flower. Gently tap your bee around the bottom of the flower. Your bee is drinking nectar and gathering pollen.

5. Fly your bee to a new flower. Choose one with a different color of glitter. Gently tap your bee around the bottom of that flower.

6. Fly your bee to two more flowers. Make sure you visit a flower with every color of glitter.

7. Return to the first flower. Look inside. Do you see pollen from other flowers? (Look for glitter of other colors.) If so, your flower was pollinated!

8. Think: The job of flowers is to attract pollinators. Why is that job important? Why are bees important to flowers? Why are flowers important to bees?

© Scholastic Inc.

1. Do Steps 2–7 of the investigation. Do you see "pollen" from other flowers?

_____

2. Think: Why is it important for flowers to attract pollinators?

_____

_____

3. Why are bees important to flowers?

_____

_____

4. Why are flowers important to bees?

_____

_____

_____

Investigation 2

Different animals help move pollen from flower to flower. But each animal likes a different kind of flower. Design a flower to attract a pollinator.

1. Look at the four pollinators on the next page. Choose a pollinator and design a flower for that animal. Look at the list of things it likes. Draw a flower for your pollinator on the next page.

2. Gather materials and make a flower for your pollinator. Think about color. Think about shape. Think about smell.

3. Pick a different pollinator. Find a flower that it would like. Draw it on a separate sheet of paper. Write about which pollinator you think would like it and why.

Materials

★ things to make a flower (colored paper, markers, crayons, scissors, tape)

★ a sweet-smelling liquid, like vanilla extract (optional)

★ a fruity-smelling liquid, like lemon extract (optional)

★ crayons or markers

★ recording sheet (next page)

What Pollinators Like

Bee
★ a place it can land (like a petal)
★ yellow or blue color
★ sweet smell

Butterfly
★ a place it can land (like a petal)
★ tiny tubes for butterfly tongues to gather nectar
★ pink or light purple color
★ sweet smell

Beetle
★ large flower
★ flat or dish-shaped flower (easy for beetle to climb on)
★ green or white color
★ spicy or fruity smell

Hummingbird
★ long tube shape (big enough for the bird's head and beak)
★ red or orange color
★ no smell needed

1. Do Step 1 of the investigation. Draw a flower for your pollinator.

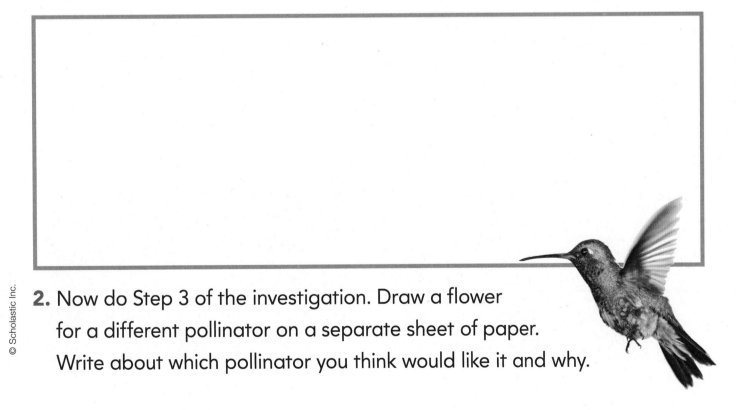

2. Now do Step 3 of the investigation. Draw a flower for a different pollinator on a separate sheet of paper. Write about which pollinator you think would like it and why.

Which Insect Is It?

Read the article about insects. Then follow the directions in the box.

Is it a **butterfly**? Or is it a **moth**? Both kinds of insects are colorful. Most butterflies have bright colors. Moths have pale colors.

Butterflies and moths need to keep warm. But they keep warm in different ways. A butterfly warms itself in the sun. A moth warms up by moving its wings.

Both insects fly. Butterflies fly in the day. But moths fly at night.

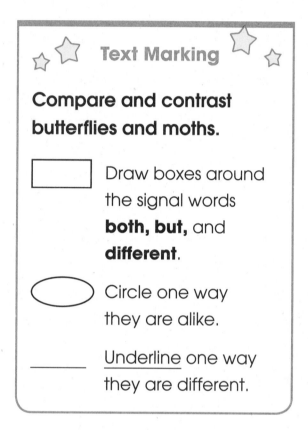

★ **Text Marking** ★

Compare and contrast butterflies and moths.

☐ Draw boxes around the signal words **both, but,** and **different**.

⬭ Circle one way they are alike.

__ Underline one way they are different.

Butterfly

Moth

© Scholastic Inc.

Answer each question. Use the article and photos.

1. This article compares and contrasts _____.

 ○ A. day and night

 ○ B. moths and butterflies

 ○ C. flying and resting

What helped you answer?

_____

_____

2. What does a moth do to stay warm?

 ○ A. It rests in the sun.

 ○ B. It flaps its wings.

 ○ C. It sleeps under its wings.

What helped you answer?

_____

_____

3. What is another way that butterflies and moths are different?

_____

_____

Auks and Hawks

Read the article about birds. Then follow the directions in the box.

Auks and **hawks** are birds. Like all birds, both lay eggs. Both fly and hunt.

In other ways, auks and hawks are different. Auks are black and white. Hawks come in many colors.

Auks have short legs with webbed feet. Hawks have long, strong legs. They have sharp claws.

Auks eat fish and other sea life. Hawks eat small land animals, snakes, and insects.

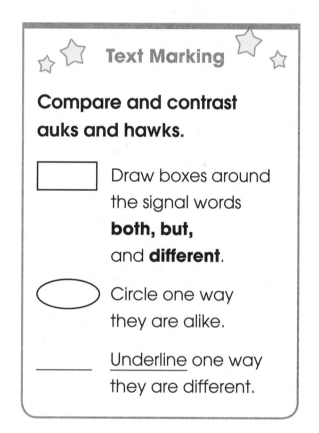

Text Marking

Compare and contrast auks and hawks.

☐ Draw boxes around the signal words **both, but,** and **different**.

⬭ Circle one way they are alike.

___ Underline one way they are different.

Auk

Hawk

Answer each question. Use the article and photos.

1. This article compares and contrasts _____.

    ○ A. claws and webbed feet

    ○ B. birds and fish

    ○ C. hawks and auks

What helped you answer?

_____

_____

2. Which is a way that auks and hawks are ALIKE?

    ○ A. Both eat snakes.

    ○ B. Both lay eggs.

    ○ C. Both have long legs.

What helped you answer?

_____

_____

3. Look at the photos. Which is the hawk? Which is the auk?
Write how you can tell.

_____

_____

Name That Dinosaur

Write the dinosaur name that goes with each clue.

I am one of the longest dinosaurs.

— — — — — — —
__6__ __4__

I am the fiercest dinosaur.

__3__ — — — — — — — — — — __2__

I am a spike-tailed dinosaur.

— — — — — — — — —
__7__

I am a three-horned dinosaur.

— — — — — — — — —
__1__

I am a duck-billed dinosaur.

— — — — — — — — —
__5__

Trachodon

Brachiosaurus

Tyrannosaurus rex

Triceratops

Stegosaurus

Use the letters above to finish the rhyme.

**Dinosaurs were amazing creatures, I think
But I'll never see a real one because they are . . .**

◯ ◯ ◯ ◯ ◯ ◯ ◯ !
1 2 3 4 5 6 7

Plants We Eat

Read the paragraph. Then answer the questions.

We eat many foods that come from plants.

Do you eat apples and bananas?

They are fruits. Do you eat toast or cereal?

They are made from grains like wheat,

oats, and rice. How about carrots,

celery, and potatoes? They are vegetables.

Fruits, grains, and vegetables all come from plants.

1. The main idea of this paragraph is
- ○ A. cereal is made from grains.
- ○ B. carrots are vegetables.
- ○ C. many foods we eat come from plants.

2. Apples are
- ○ A. vegetables.
- ○ B. fruits.
- ○ C. grains.

3. If you eat a banana on cereal, you eat
- ○ A. fruit and grains.
- ○ B. two vegetables.
- ○ C. plants and animals.

Thumbs Up!

**Read the article about the human body.
Then follow the directions in the box.**

Thumbs are special fingers. All your fingers can move in and out. All can move from side to side. All can bend and wiggle. All can move in a circle. But only a thumb can touch every other fingertip. No other fingers can meet like this. Try it. Your thumbs help you grab and hold things. Can you pick up a penny without using your thumb?

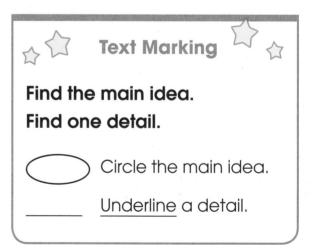

Text Marking

Find the main idea.
Find one detail.

⬭ Circle the main idea.

___ <u>Underline</u> a detail.

Answer each question. Use the article and photo.

1. Which is something ONLY thumbs can do?

    ○ A. bend and wiggle

    ○ B. move in a circle

    ○ C. touch every other fingertip

What helped you answer?

_____

_____

2. What do your thumbs help you do?

    ○ A. wiggle   ○ B. pick things up   ○ C. count pennies

What helped you answer?

_____

_____

3. Try to pick up a penny without using your thumb. What happens? Write about it.

_____

_____

Ahhh . . .choo!

Read the health article. Then follow the directions in the box.

Almost anything can cause a sneeze. You might breathe in some dust, cold air, or even pepper. It tickles the inside of your nose. So you need to clear it out.

Your brain gets the message. It signals some muscles to get ready to help. When they do, you suddenly feel the results. Your eyes close tight. Your mouth opens, and you sneeze: AHHH…CHOO! The tickle is gone.

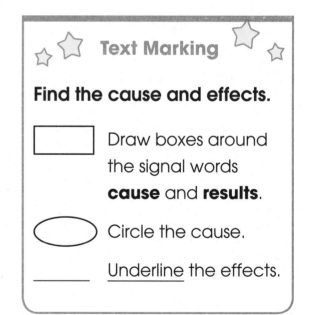

☆☆ **Text Marking** ☆☆

Find the cause and effects.

☐ Draw boxes around the signal words **cause** and **results**.

◯ Circle the cause.

___ Underline the effects.

Answer each question. Use the article and photo.

1. What does your brain do when your nose feels a tickle inside?

○ A. It sends messages to muscles that can help.

○ B. It removes dust from your nose.

○ C. It makes you feel sleepy.

What helped you answer?

_____

_____

2. Which is NOT an effect of having a tickle inside your nose?

○ A. You sneeze.

○ B. Your mouth opens.

○ C. You feel ticklish all over.

What helped you answer?

_____

_____

3. How does sneezing make you feel better?

_____

_____

The Four Seasons

Circle the season that goes with each sentence.

1. Birds make nests for babies.

2. Children build snowmen.

3. Leaves turn red, orange, and yellow.

4. Children go swimming outside.

5. Flowers begin to bloom.

6. Some animals hibernate.

7. Trees start losing leaves.

8. Insects fly through the air.

Did you notice a pattern in the answers? Draw the pattern in the squares.

The Changing Seasons

Read about the four seasons. Then try the science investigations.

Spring! The sun stays out a long time. The air gets warmer. What a nice change from the cold, dark winter. Plants start to bloom. Insects come out. So do animals that count on them for food.

In the **summer**, the weather gets hotter. There's still plenty of food. But little by little, the sun rises later and sets earlier.

In **autumn** the air gets cooler. Leaves change colors. They fall off trees. Some animals gather as much food as they can. Others travel to warmer places.

The days are short and cold. **Winter** has come! Most plants and trees are bare. There's hardly any food to eat. Animals take shelter to keep warm. Others **hibernate**, or go into deep sleep. Maybe they're dreaming of spring!

Investigation 1

Keep track of how long or short the days are.

Is it spring, summer, fall, or winter? Your calendar may tell you. But you can also find your own clues to the season.

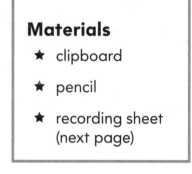

Materials
* ★ clipboard
* ★ pencil
* ★ recording sheet (next page)

1. Gather your materials.

2. Write the current season on the next page. (If you need to, ask an adult for help.)

3. **Think:** What would you expect the weather to be like during this season? What would plants look like? What would animals be doing? What would people be wearing or doing? Write or draw your answers on your recording sheet.

4. Now go outside. Look for clues about each item on your list. Write or draw what you found on your recording sheet.

5. Pick one other season. What do you think would be different if you looked for clues in that season?

Current season: _____

	What I expect...	Clues I found...
Weather		
Plants		
Animals		
People		

Pick a different season. What do you think would be different if you looked for clues in that season? Write your answer on a separate sheet of paper.

Investigation 2

Keep track of how long or short the days are.

Materials

★ pencils

★ recording sheet (next page)

1. Look at the Season Tracker. How many seasons do you see? How many months do you see?

2. Find the current month. What season is it? (**Hint:** Look to the right of the month.) Are the days getting longer or shorter? During which seasons are the days getting longer? During which seasons are the days getting shorter?

3. The length of a day is the time between sunrise and sunset. Look up the times of today's sunrise and sunset. Write the times in the chart on the next page.

4. Predict: In one week, what will be the times for sunrise and sunset? Record your guesses.

5. Wait one week. Find the actual times for sunrise and sunset. Record your results.

6. Do Steps 4 and 5 again for the following week. Look at your chart. What do you notice?

Season Tracker

Month	Season
January	**Winter** Days are getting longer.
February	
March	Spring Equinox — Day and night are equal
April	**Spring** Days are getting longer.
May	
June	Summer Solstice — Longest day and shortest night
July	**Summer** Days are getting shorter.
August	
September	Fall Equinox — Day and night are equal
October	**Fall** Days are getting shorter.
November	
December	Winter Solstice — Shortest day and longest night

1. What season is it? _____

2. Are the days getting longer or shorter? _____

3. During which seasons are the days getting longer?

_____

4. During which seasons are the days getting shorter?

_____

5. Record the times for sunrise and sunset in the chart below.

	Sunrise time	**Sunset time**
Today's date: _____		
Date (one week later): _____	I predict: _____ Actual time: _____	I predict: _____ Actual time: _____
Date (two weeks later): _____	I predict: _____ Actual time: _____	I predict: _____ Actual time: _____

High Waters

Read the article. Then follow the directions in the box.

A **flood** happens when water
spills over. What causes a flood?
Snow melts off mountains in the spring.
It turns into water.
The water runs downhill.
It flows into rivers.
Rainstorms add more water to rivers.
Rivers can't hold all that extra water.
So they **overflow**.
The water covers everything nearby.
Floods soak fields, roads, and towns.

A flooded home

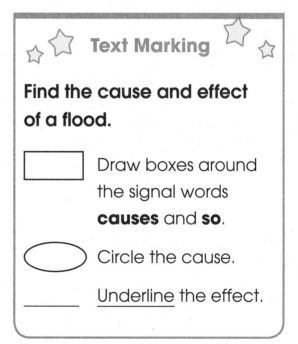

★ **Text Marking** ★

Find the cause and effect of a flood.

☐ Draw boxes around the signal words **causes** and **so**.

◯ Circle the cause.

___ Underline the effect.

© Scholastic Inc.

Answer each question. Use the article and photo.

1. The word **overflow** means _____.

○ A. heat up   ○ B. spill over   ○ C. get cold

What helped you answer?

_____

_____

2. Which does NOT cause floods?

○ A. rain   ○ B. melting snow   ○ C. fields and towns

What helped you answer?

_____

_____

3. Why do you think most floods happen in spring?

_____

_____

_____

_____

Weather Watchers

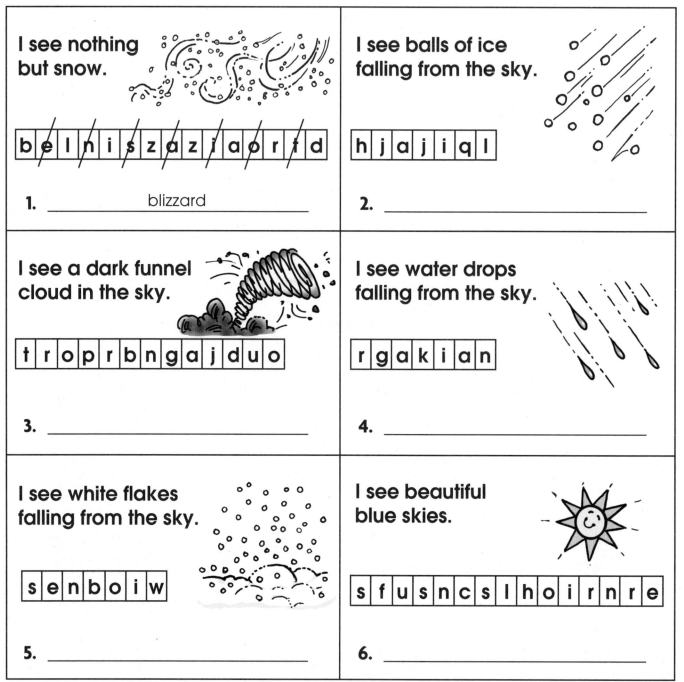

Look at the weather picture. Read the weather clue.
Cross out every other letter box. The letters left will
name the kind of weather. Write the weather word on the line.
The first one has been done or you.

I see nothing but snow.

| b | e̶ | l | n̶ | i | s̶ | z | a̶ | z | f̶ | a | o̶ | r | f̶ | d |

1. _____blizzard_____

I see balls of ice falling from the sky.

| h | j | a | j | i | q | l |

2. _____

I see a dark funnel cloud in the sky.

| t | r | o | p | r | b | n | g | a | j | d | u | o |

3. _____

I see water drops falling from the sky.

| r | g | a | k | i | a | n |

4. _____

I see white flakes falling from the sky.

| s | e | n | b | o | i | w |

5. _____

I see beautiful blue skies.

| s | f | u | s | n | c | s | l | h | o | i | r | n | r | e |

6. _____

© Scholastic Inc.

Powerful Push

Read about wind. Then try the science investigations.

Wind is moving air. Its force can blow your hat off your head. It can turn your umbrella inside out. Very strong storm winds can even blow the roof off a house.

We can't control the wind. But people have learned how to use the wind's power. We can use it to sail boats. We can use it to keep kites high in the air. We can even use it to make electricity for our homes. How else can we use wind?

Investigation 1

Use wind power to give this toy a push!

1. Gather the materials you will need.

2. Look at the square below. Use it as a guide to make your own spin wheel. Follow these steps:

- Use a ruler to draw a square that measures 4 inches tall by 4 inches wide on a separate sheet of paper.
- Copy the shapes and dashed lines onto your own square.
- Cut out the square.

3. With the printed side up, fold it in half so the bottom edge meets the top edge. Unfold.

4. Fold it in half again so the right edge meets the left edge. Unfold.

5. Flip the paper over so the blank side is up. Fold one corner to its opposite corner. Unfold.

6. Fold so that the other two corners meet. Unfold.

7. Flip the paper over. Gently push on all four circles. The middle of the paper should poke up in a point.

8. Hold a pencil with the tip pointing up. Balance the folded paper on the tip.

9. You can blow air at the Spin Wheel to give it a push. **Predict:** Which parts of the Spin Wheel could you push (or blow) to make it spin?

Materials

- ★ sheet of paper
- ★ pencil
- ★ ruler
- ★ scissors
- ★ recording sheet (next page)

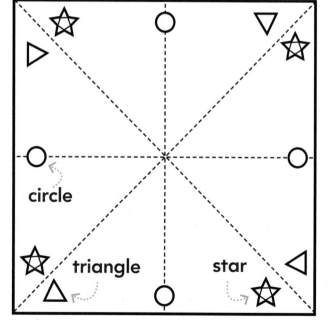

circle

triangle   star

© Scholastic Inc.

1. Do Steps 2–7 of the investigation.

Predict: Which parts of the Spin Wheel could you push (blow on) to make it spin? Check any of the boxes or none.

☐ the stars   ☐ straight down on the top

☐ the circles   ☐ straight up from the bottom

☐ the triangles

2. Test your predictions. Which worked best to turn the Spin Wheel?

_____

_____

3. Try to make the Spin Wheel turn slowly. Try to make it turn quickly. How did you do it? Use the words *push* and *power* in your writing.

_____

_____

Investigation 2

**What would help your toy catch the wind better?
Try this!**

Materials
★ tracing paper
★ ruler
★ pencil
★ scissors
★ tape
★ inventor's materials: paper, index cards, straws, pipe cleaners, egg cartons, plastic wrap, store-bought feathers
★ recording sheet (next page)

1. Gather the materials you will need.

2. Follow these steps to make a Super Spinner:
   - Trace the circle below onto a separate sheet of paper. Copy all lines and shading.
   - Cut out the circle. Then cut along the dotted lines.
   - Line up the cut edge with the solid line. The gray pattern will be covered up. The two halves of the star will line up.
   - Tape down the edges.

3. Put your cone over a pencil point. Blow on it gently. What happens?

4. **Think:** How could you change your cone to make it spin like a Spin Wheel? (**Hint:** You can cut and fold it. You can tape new pieces on to it.) Write down three ideas that might work.

5. Pick one of your ideas and test it. (**Hint:** It's important to keep your changes balanced. If you add things to only one side, the cone will fall off the pencil!) If your idea works, think of ways to make it even better. If it doesn't work, pick a different idea to test.

6. Write about your best design. Why can it spin when you blow on it? Did you run into any problems? How did you fix them?

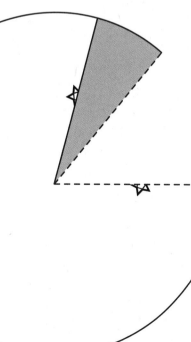

© Scholastic Inc.

1. Do Steps 2 and 3 of the investigation. What happens when you blow on your Super Spinner Cone?

_____

_____

2. Think: How could you change your cone to make it spin like a Spin Wheel? Write down three ideas that might work.

Idea 1: _____

_____

Idea 2: _____

_____

Idea 3: _____

_____

Fanciful Flowers

Use the words to label the picture.
Then use the shape code to complete the sentence below.

s̸eed   stem   fl⬜wer   rai⬡n   le△af
roo⬡t s   so⬜i l   ⬡bug   sunligh⬡t

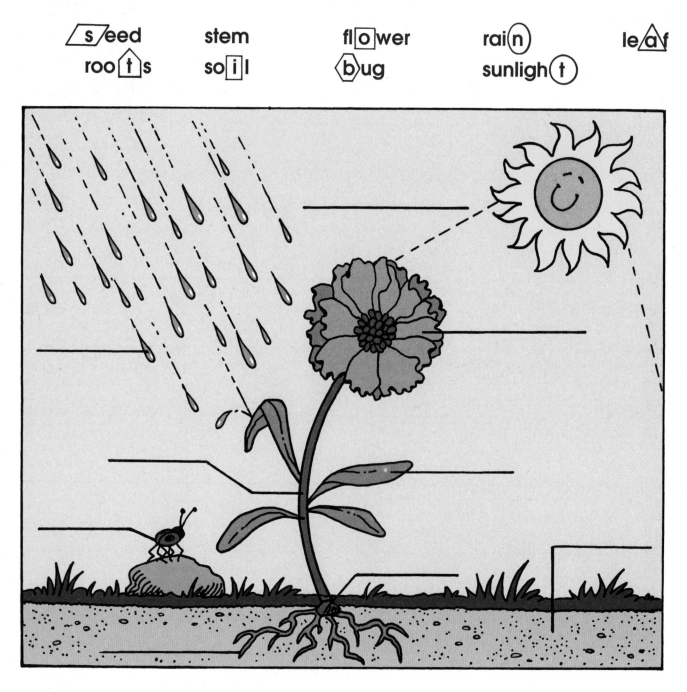

A person who enjoys learning about flowers is a

⬡ ⬜ ◯ △ ⬭ ▢ ▱ ⌂ .

Out of This World

Use the grid to identify each planet.

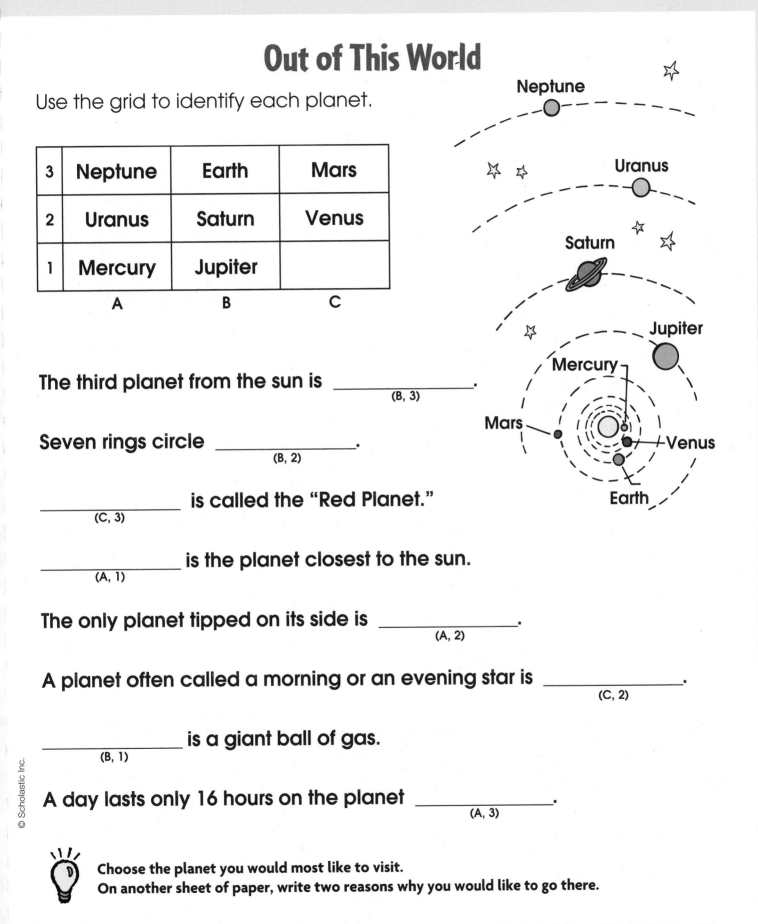

3	Neptune	Earth	Mars
2	Uranus	Saturn	Venus
1	Mercury	Jupiter	
	A	B	C

The third planet from the sun is _____.
(B, 3)

Seven rings circle _____.
(B, 2)

_____ is called the "Red Planet."
(C, 3)

_____ is the planet closest to the sun.
(A, 1)

The only planet tipped on its side is _____.
(A, 2)

A planet often called a morning or an evening star is _____.
(C, 2)

_____ is a giant ball of gas.
(B, 1)

A day lasts only 16 hours on the planet _____.
(A, 3)

Choose the planet you would most like to visit.
On another sheet of paper, write two reasons why you would like to go there.

What's on Mars?

Read the paragraph. Then answer the questions.

The planet Mars is called the Red Planet.

That's because it is covered in reddish dust.

How did scientists learn what Mars is like?

They sent a robot to Mars.

The robot collected rocks and dirt.

It also took pictures and sent them back to Earth.

Scientists studied the rocks, dirt, and pictures.

They learned that Mars is cold and **dry**.

1. What did the robot do after it took pictures?
- ○ A. It collected rocks.
- ○ B. It sent them to Earth.
- ○ C. It landed on Mars.

2. The pictures must have showed that Mars is
- ○ A. hot.
- ○ B. wet.
- ○ C. red.

3. The word dry in this paragraph means
- ○ A. dirty.
- ○ B. not wet.
- ○ C. rocky.

Clowning Around

Add. Color the picture
using the color code.

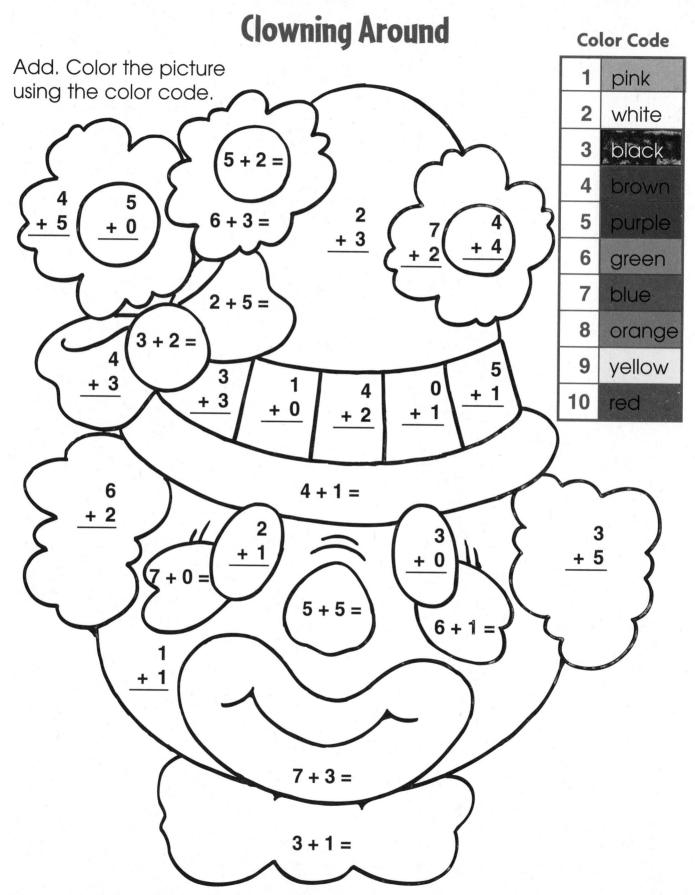

1	pink
2	white
3	black
4	brown
5	purple
6	green
7	blue
8	orange
9	yellow
10	red

$5 + 2 =$

$6 + 3 =$

$\begin{array}{r} 4 \\ + 5 \\ \hline \end{array}$ $\begin{array}{r} 5 \\ + 0 \\ \hline \end{array}$

$\begin{array}{r} 2 \\ + 3 \\ \hline \end{array}$

$\begin{array}{r} 7 \\ + 2 \\ \hline \end{array}$ $\begin{array}{r} 4 \\ + 4 \\ \hline \end{array}$

$2 + 5 =$

$3 + 2 =$

$\begin{array}{r} 4 \\ + 3 \\ \hline \end{array}$

$\begin{array}{r} 3 \\ + 3 \\ \hline \end{array}$ $\begin{array}{r} 1 \\ + 0 \\ \hline \end{array}$ $\begin{array}{r} 4 \\ + 2 \\ \hline \end{array}$ $\begin{array}{r} 0 \\ + 1 \\ \hline \end{array}$ $\begin{array}{r} 5 \\ + 1 \\ \hline \end{array}$

$4 + 1 =$

$\begin{array}{r} 6 \\ + 2 \\ \hline \end{array}$

$\begin{array}{r} 2 \\ + 1 \\ \hline \end{array}$

$7 + 0 =$

$\begin{array}{r} 3 \\ + 0 \\ \hline \end{array}$

$\begin{array}{r} 3 \\ + 5 \\ \hline \end{array}$

$5 + 5 =$

$6 + 1 =$

$\begin{array}{r} 1 \\ + 1 \\ \hline \end{array}$

$7 + 3 =$

$3 + 1 =$

Lovely Ladybugs

Write a number sentence to show how many spots each ladybug has.

💡 **Color the ladybug with the greatest number of spots red.**
Color the ladybug with the least number of spots blue.

Beautiful Bouquets

Look at the number on each bow. Draw more flowers to match the number written on the bow.

Color the bows with an even number yellow.
Color the bows with an odd number purple.

Telephone Math

What kind of phone never rings? _____

To find out, solve the addition problems. Then use the code on the telephone to replace your answers with letters. The first one has been done for you.

1 E	2 N	3 O
4 H	5 N	6 S
7 P	8 A	9 X
* H	0 T	# R

$$\begin{array}{r} 6 \\ + 2 \\ \hline 8 \end{array}$$ A

$$\begin{array}{r} 5 \\ + 1 \\ \hline \end{array}$$ _____

$$\begin{array}{r} 4 \\ + 4 \\ \hline \end{array}$$ _____

$$\begin{array}{r} 3 \\ + 6 \\ \hline \end{array}$$ _____

$$\begin{array}{r} 3 \\ + 0 \\ \hline \end{array}$$ _____

$$\begin{array}{r} 3 \\ + 4 \\ \hline \end{array}$$ _____

$$\begin{array}{r} 2 \\ + 2 \\ \hline \end{array}$$ _____

$$\begin{array}{r} 2 \\ + 1 \\ \hline \end{array}$$ _____

$$\begin{array}{r} 1 \\ + 1 \\ \hline \end{array}$$ _____

$$\begin{array}{r} 0 \\ + 1 \\ \hline \end{array}$$ _____

Write your telephone number in letters using the phone code above.

_____

High Flyer

Do the subtraction problems.

If the answer is 1 or 2, color the shape red.

If the answer is 3 or 4, color the shape blue.

If the answer is 5 or 6, color the shape yellow.

If the answer is 7 or 8, color the shape green.

If the answer is 9, color the shape black.

Color the other shapes the colors of your choice.

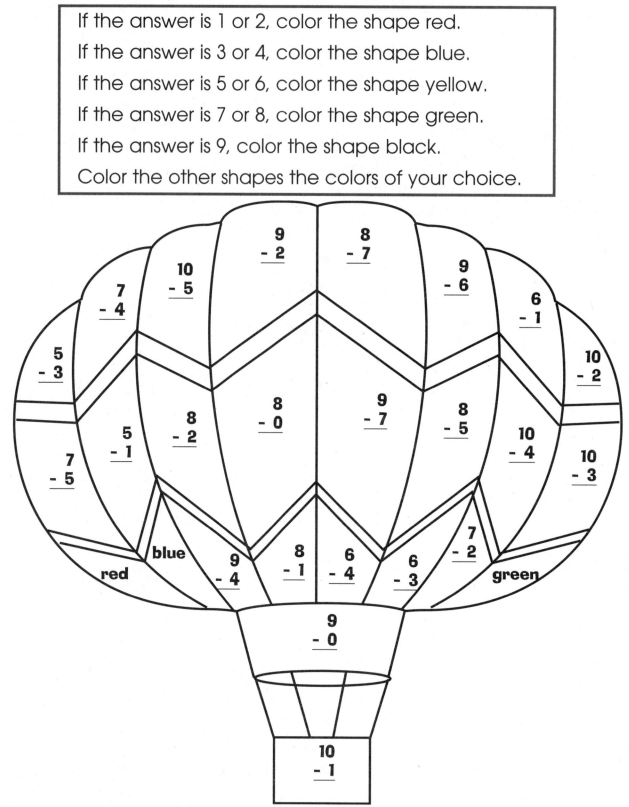

Juggling Act

Cross out. Write how many are left.

4 – 2 = _____

3 – 1 = _2_

7 – 4 = _____

9 – 6 = _____   5 – 3 = _____   6 – 5 = _____

Ocean Life

Use the math picture on the next page to count and write the number in each box. Subtract the numbers.

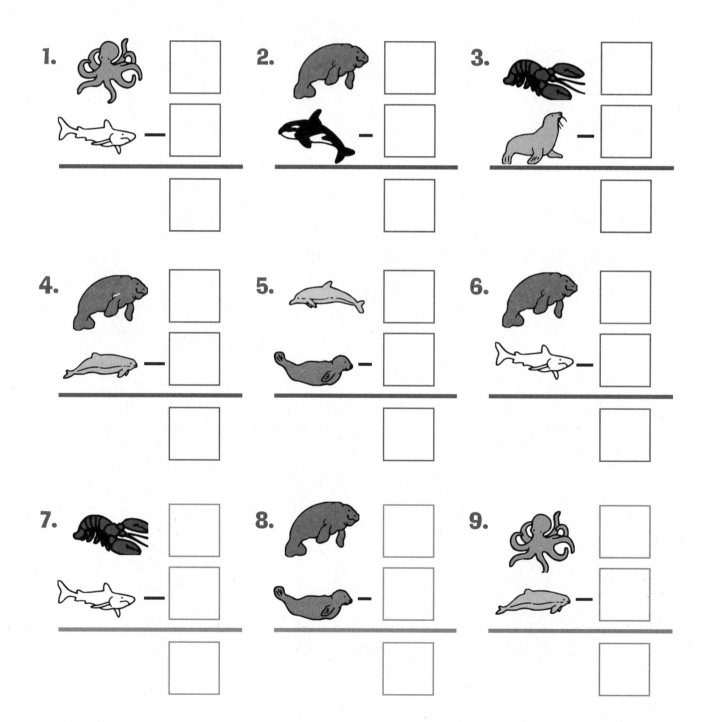

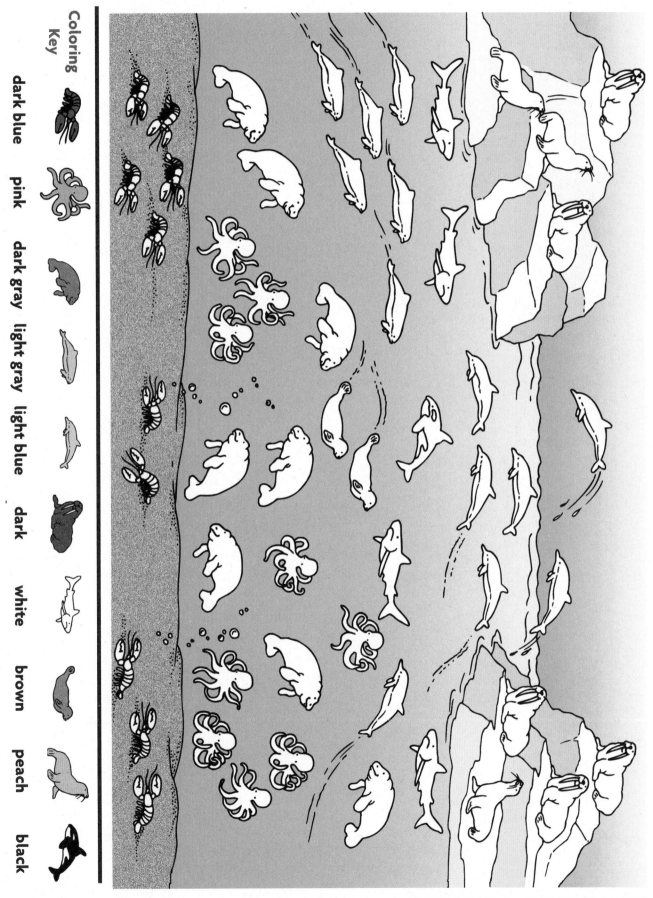

Coloring Key

dark blue
pink
dark gray
light gray
light blue
dark
white
brown
peach
black

Trucking Along

Subtract. Color the picture using the color code.

Color Code

0	white
1	brown
2	black
3	green
4	purple
5	orange
6	yellow
7	blue
8	red

Night Lights

Subtract. Connect the dots from greatest to least.

10 – 3 = ☐ •

9 – 1 = ☐   8 – 2 = ☐

10 – 1 = ☐ •   • 9 – 4 = ☐

10 – 0 = ☐ •   • 7 – 3 = ☐

5 – 3 = ☐

6 – 5 = ☐ •   • 8 – 5 = ☐

Subtract. Connect the dots from least to greatest.

10 – 0 = ☐ • - - - • 9 – 8 = ☐

• 7 – 5 = ☐

10 – 1 = ☐ •

• 10 – 7 = ☐

10 – 2 = ☐ •

The top picture gives off its own light. Color this picture orange. The bottom picture reflects light from the sun. Color this picture yellow.

7 – 0 = ☐ •   • 6 – 2 = ☐

9 – 3 = ☐ •   • 9 – 4 = ☐

Hop to It: Add and Subtract

Add or subtract. Trace the number line with your finger to check your work.

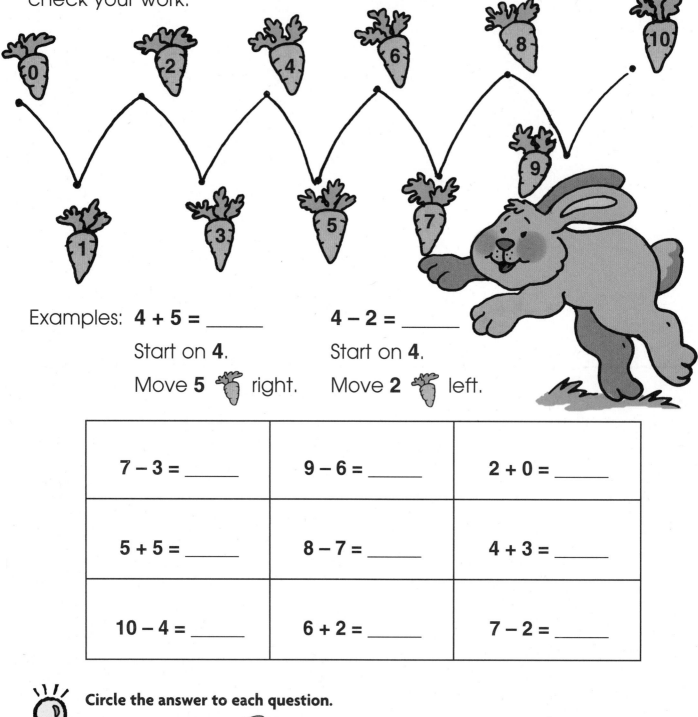

Examples: **4 + 5 = _____**   **4 − 2 = _____**

Start on **4**.   Start on **4**.

Move **5** 🥕 right.   Move **2** 🥕 left.

7 − 3 = _____	**9 − 6 = _____**	**2 + 0 = _____**
5 + 5 = _____	**8 − 7 = _____**	**4 + 3 = _____**
10 − 4 = _____	**6 + 2 = _____**	**7 − 2 = _____**

Circle the answer to each question.

What direction did 🐰 **move to add?**   left or right

What direction did 🐰 **move to subtract?**   left or right

© Scholastic Inc.

Mitten Matchup

Add or subtract. Draw a line to match mittens with the same answer.

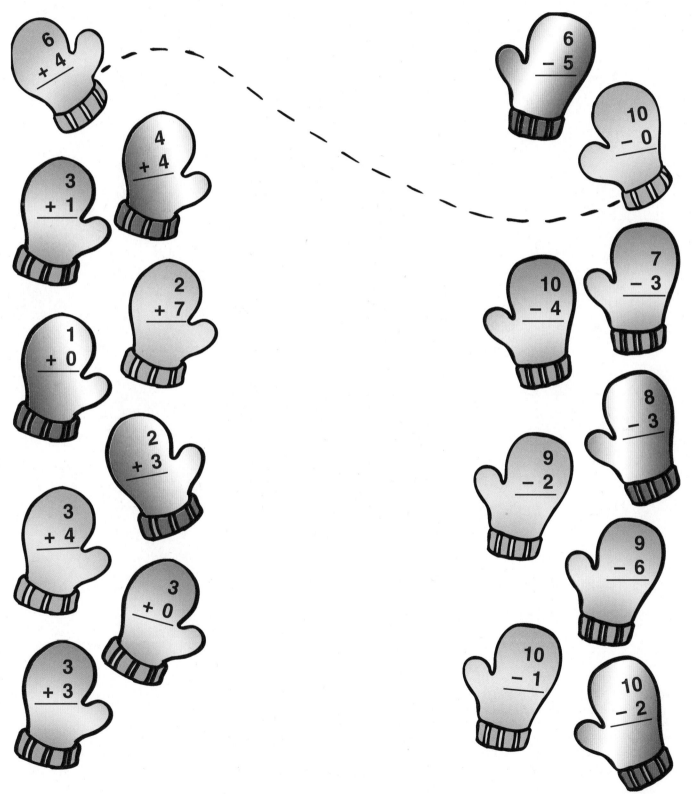

Blast Off

Add or subtract. Then use the code to answer the riddle below.

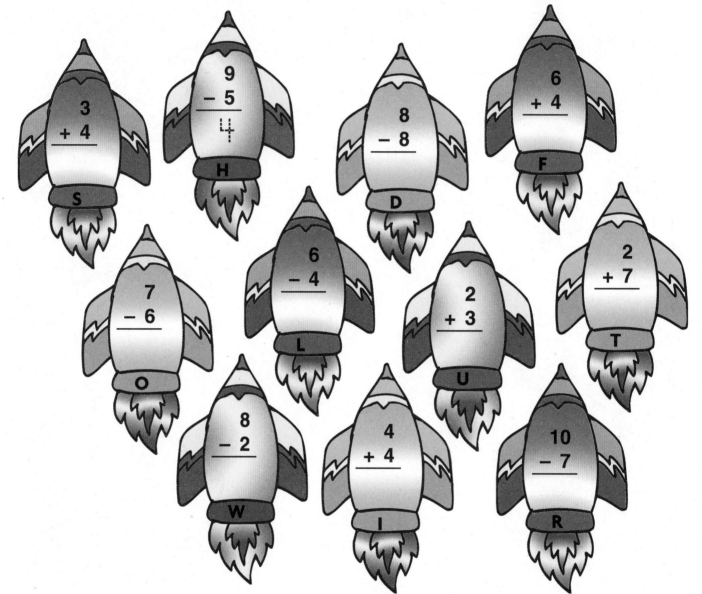

- $3 + 4 =$ **S**
- $9 - 5 = 4$ **H**
- $8 - 8 =$ **D**
- $6 + 4 =$ **F**
- $7 - 6 =$ **O**
- $6 - 4 =$ **L**
- $2 + 3 =$ **U**
- $2 + 7 =$ **T**
- $8 - 2 =$ **W**
- $4 + 4 =$ **I**
- $10 - 7 =$ **R**

How is an astronaut's job unlike any other job?

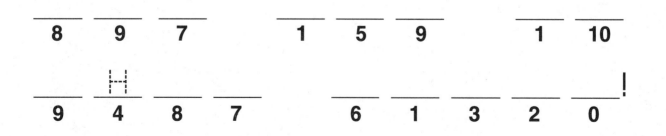

```
___ ___ ___'   ___ ___ ___   ___ ___
 8   9   7     1   5   9     1   10

___  H  ___ ___   ___ ___ ___ ___ ___!
 9   4   8   7    6   1   3   2   0
```

Out on the Town

Color a box on the graph for each item in the picture.

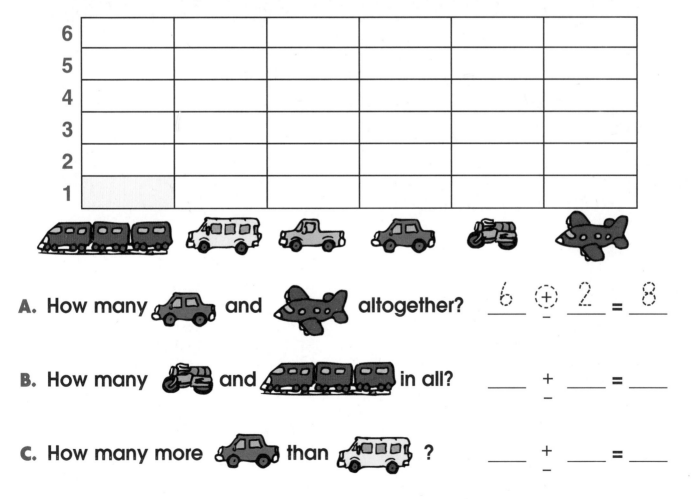

A. How many [car] and [plane] altogether? $6 \oplus 2 = 8$

B. How many [motorcycle] and [train] in all? ___ + ___ = ___

C. How many more [car] than [bus] ? ___ + ___ = ___

Shapes on a Snake

Add or subtract.

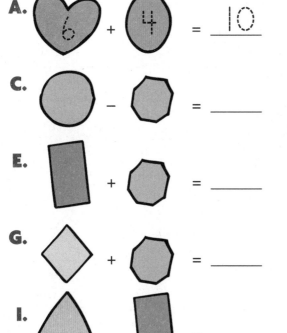

A. 6 + 4 = 10

B. ☐ − ◇ = ____

C. ◯ − ⬡ = ____

D. ◯ + ♥ = ____

E. ▭ + ⬡ = ____

F. ⬡ + ⬡ = ____

G. ◇ + ⬡ = ____

H. ♥ + ◯ = ____

I. △ − ▭ = ____

J. ☐ − ⬡ = ____

Planes ... Trains ...

Add or subtract.

A. There are **7** cars in the parking lot. Then **3** more cars park there, too. How many cars are there in all in the lot?

$\underline{7} \; ⊕ \; \underline{3} = \underline{10}$ cars

B. There are **7** boxes on the truck. Then **4** boxes fall on the street. How many boxes are left on the truck?

_____ + _____ = _____ boxes

C. There are **10** planes waiting on the runway. Then **6** planes take off. How many planes are left on the runway?

_____ + _____ = _____ planes

D. There are **8** girls and **2** boys on the bus. How many more girls than boys are on the bus?

_____ + _____ = _____ more girls

E. There are **5** people in the first car and **4** people in the second car. How many people in all?

_____ + _____ = _____ people

Slice It Up

Add. Color the picture using the color code.

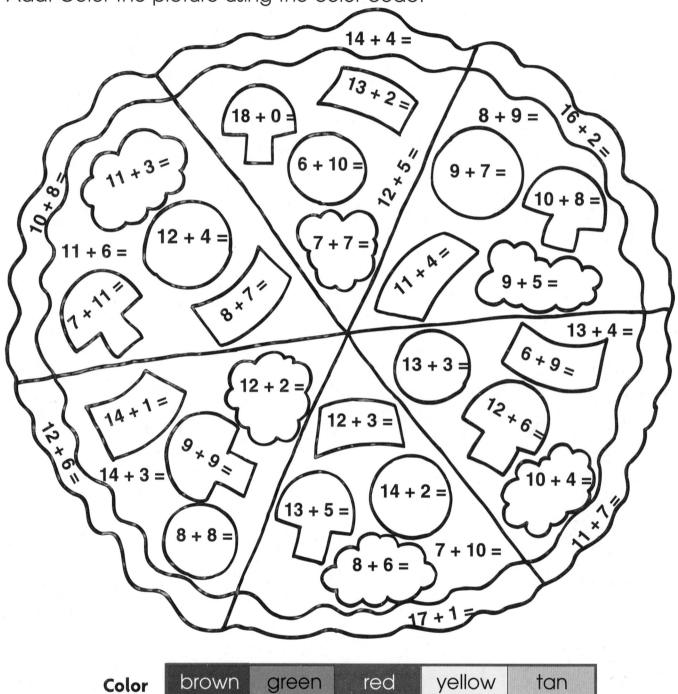

Color	brown	green	red	yellow	tan
Code	14	15	16	17	18

How many different ways can you make a sum of 10? Show your work on another piece of paper.

Leap on Over

Add. To show the frog's path across the pond, color each lily pad green if the sum is greater than 10.

10 + 1 =

6 + 4 =

6 + 9 =

5 + 2 =

7 + 0 =

5 + 5 =

9 + 2 =

10 + 4 =

3 + 7 =

7 + 6 =

4 + 3 =

5 + 4 =

3 + 8 =

2 + 2 =

8 + 8 =

How many leaps did the frog take across the pond? _____

Animal Mystery

What kind of animal always carries a trunk?

To find out, solve the addition problems. If the answer is greater than 9, color the shape yellow. If the answer is less than 10, color the shape gray.

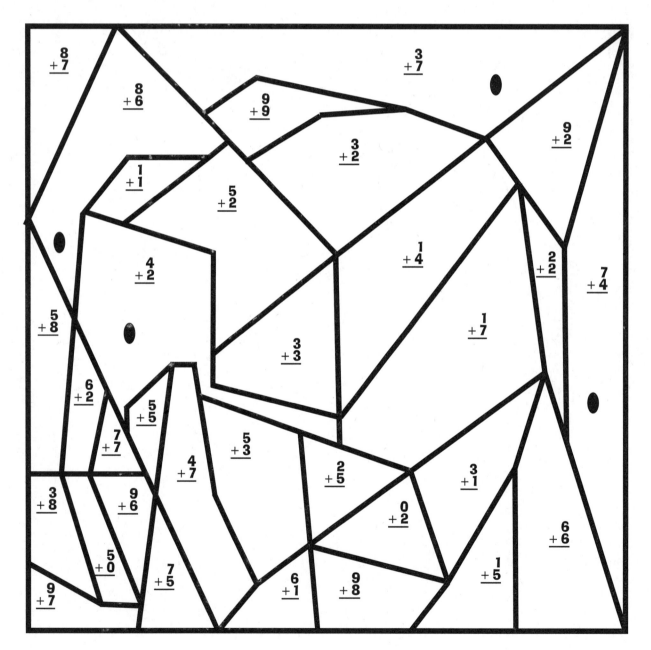

Scarecrow Sam

Why doesn't Scarecrow Sam tell secrets when he is near Farmer Joe's bean patch?

To find out the answer, add the numbers. Circle the pumpkins that have sums of 14, and write the letters that appear inside those pumpkins in the boxes below.

1. 4 + 2 G
2. 7 + 7 B
3. 9 + 5 E
4. 10 + 4 A
5. 4 + 8 R
6. 6 + 8 N
7. 11 + 3 S
8. 14 + 0 T
9. 7 + 2 P
10. 13 + 1 A
11. 5 + 8 S
12. 12 + 2 L
13. 7 + 4 H
14. 5 + 9 K

Flying High

Add down and across to find the missing number.

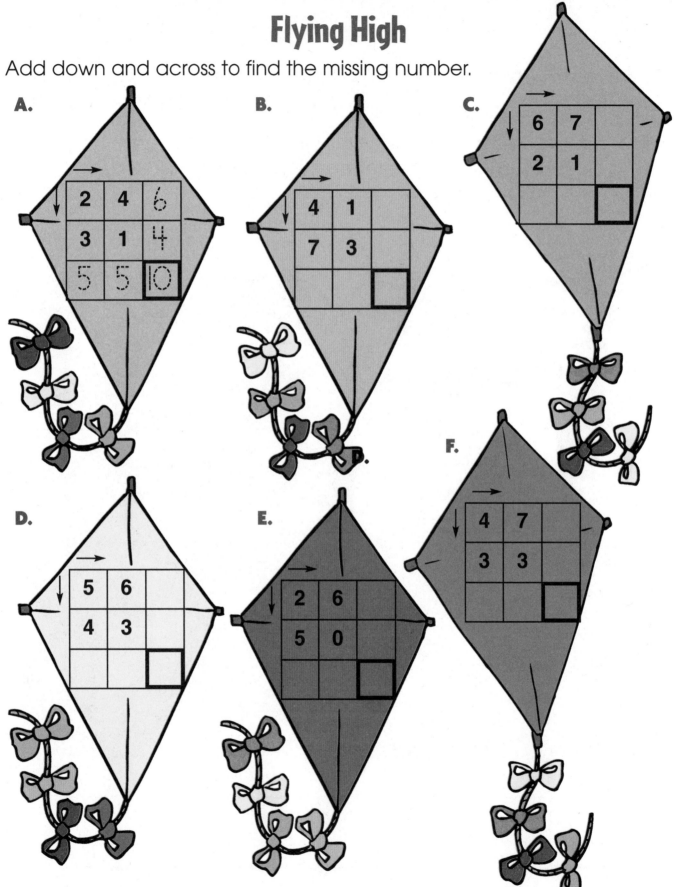

A.

2	4	6
3	1	4
5	5	10

B.

4	1	
7	3	

C.

6	7	
2	1	

D.

5	6	
4	3	

E.

2	6	
5	0	

F.

4	7	
3	3	

Double Dips

Write the doubles that equal the number on the cone.

Circle the answer.

When adding doubles, the sum will always be: even   odd

Not Far From Home

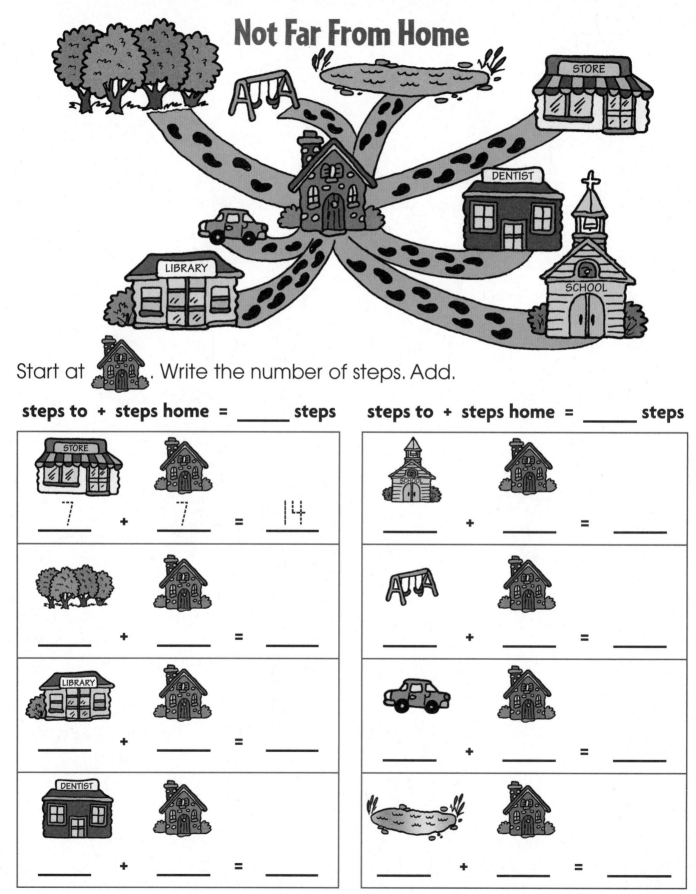

Start at 🏠. Write the number of steps. Add.

steps to + steps home = _____ steps

STORE 🏠	
__7__ + __7__ = __14__	
🌳 🏠	
_____ + _____ = _____	
LIBRARY 🏠	
_____ + _____ = _____	
DENTIST 🏠	
_____ + _____ = _____	

steps to + steps home = _____ steps

SCHOOL 🏠	
_____ + _____ = _____	
🎪 🏠	
_____ + _____ = _____	
🚗 🏠	
_____ + _____ = _____	
🏞️ 🏠	
_____ + _____ = _____	

© Scholastic Inc.

Break the Code

Subtract.

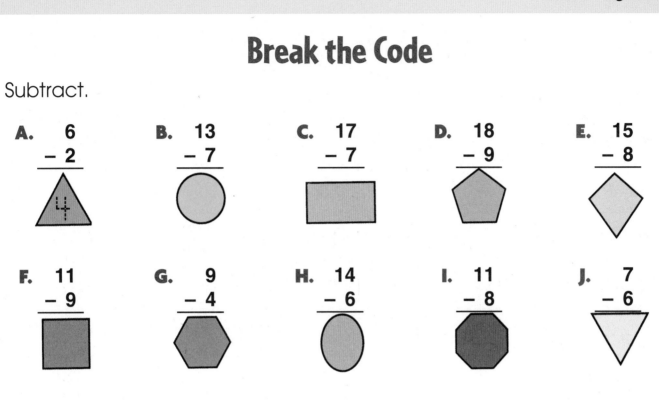

A. 6 − 2

B. 13 − 7

C. 17 − 7

D. 18 − 9

E. 15 − 8

F. 11 − 9

G. 9 − 4

H. 14 − 6

I. 11 − 8

J. 7 − 6

Use the answers above to solve each problem.

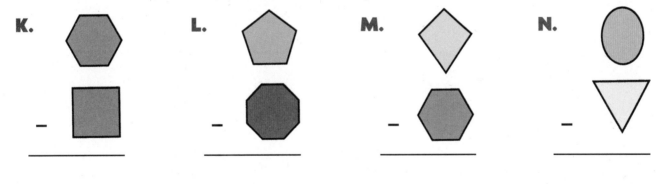

K.

L.

M.

N.

O.

P.

Q.

The Big Search

Subtract. Circle the difference.

11 − 7 = five three (four)	**14 − 9 =** nine one five
13 − 6 = six nine seven	**16 − 5 =** twelve thirteen eleven
18 − 9 = eleven ten nine	**17 − 11 =** seven six ten
15 − 5 = ten seven five	**12 − 9 =** three two four
12 − 4 = six eight nine	**11 − 9 =** three five two

Find each circled number in the word puzzle. Look → and ↓.

(f	o	u	r)	h	i	o	n	e	g	s	k	m
i	f	o	n	t	g	y	f	a	f	u	e	z
f	t	l	u	e	j	s	i	x	s	b	x	t
t	t	w	e	l	v	e	v	k	s	t	l	h
e	p	n	i	n	e	w	e	j	e	r	t	i
e	d	n	g	q	i	h	r	y	v	a	q	r
n	v	h	h	o	t	h	r	e	e	c	s	t
d	m	k	t	c	w	b	t	e	n	t	r	e
x	d	i	p	g	o	a	c	p	f	i	s	e
c	e	l	e	v	e	n	a	b	z	o	v	n
b	w	u	d	i	f	f	e	r	e	n	c	e

See if you can find these number words: twelve, fifteen, thirteen, subtraction, difference.

Race Through the Facts

Add or subtract. The race car that ends with the highest number wins the race!

$7 + 2 =$ _____ $- 4 =$ _____ $- 3 =$ _____ $+ 9 =$ _____ $+ 5 =$ _____

$12 - 3 =$ _____ $- 6 =$ _____ $+ 2 =$ _____ $+ 9 =$ _____ $- 9 =$ _____ $- 8 =$ _____ $+ 4 =$ _____

$+ 7 =$ _____ $- 6 =$ _____ $+ 3 =$ _____ $- 2 =$ _____ $+ 7 =$ _____ $+ 1 =$ _____ $+ 4 =$ _____ $- 8 =$ _____

$+ 6 =$ _____ $- 9 =$ _____ $+ 1 =$ _____

$+ 1 =$ _____ $- 11 =$ _____ $- 5 =$ _____ $+ 13 =$ _____ $- 7 =$ _____ $+ 3 =$ _____

$+ 2 =$ _____ $+ 3 =$ _____ $- 3 =$ _____

 **Color the winning race car blue.**

Little Snacks

Add or subtract. Then follow the maze through the even answers.

Start

2 + 2 =

16 – 9 =

13 – 6 =

4 + 5 =

10 – 7 =

14 – 8 =

3 + 7 =

13 – 5 =

9 + 4 =

15 – 6 =

16 – 6 =

11 + 3 =

17 – 8 =

7 + 5 =

18 – 6 =

5 + 2 =

8 + 3 =

9 + 9 =

The elephant found 9 peanuts. He ate 6 peanuts.
How many peanuts are left? _____

Flying Families

Fill in the missing number for each family. Use the numbers from the box.

6 7
13

5 7
7

7 4
(blank)

(blank) 10
18

7 8
(blank)

2 (blank)
8

9 (blank)
14

9 3
(blank)

8 2
(blank)

4 5
(blank)

(blank) 3
7

9	12	15	8	10
6	4	7	5	11	2

Fill in the families with twins.

3 3
6

14

18

10

16

Colorful Flowers

Color a box on the graph for each item in the picture.

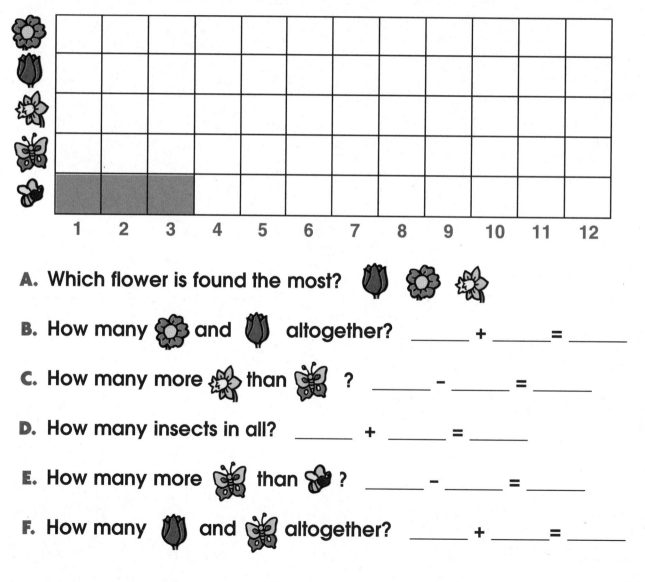

A. Which flower is found the most?

B. How many and altogether? _____ + _____ = _____

C. How many more than ? _____ − _____ = _____

D. How many insects in all? _____ + _____ = _____

E. How many more than ? _____ − _____ = _____

F. How many and altogether? _____ + _____ = _____

A Nutty Bunch

Add or subtract. Color the nut brown if the answer matches the squirrel.

A.

15 – 3 =

17 – 4 =

6 + 7 =

11 + 2 =

13

B.

8 + 3 =

15 – 4 =

9 + 3 =

18 – 7 =

11

C.

9 + 6 =

18 – 3 =

13 + 4 =

15 + 2 =

17

D.

12 + 2 =

9 + 5 =

17 – 3 =

11 + 5 =

14

Create a nutty bunch.

16

Penguin Parade

Add or subtract. Write the pattern on the flag.

5 + 7	8 + 3	15 − 5	18 − 9	11 − 3	12 − 5
9 − 7	12 − 8	5 + 1	16 − 8	13 − 3	7 + 5
12 − 9	11 − 5	13 − 4	7 + 5	18 − 3	11 + 7
15 − 2	4 + 7	12 − 3	12 − 5	8 − 3	12 − 9

A Perfect Strike

Fill in the missing number.

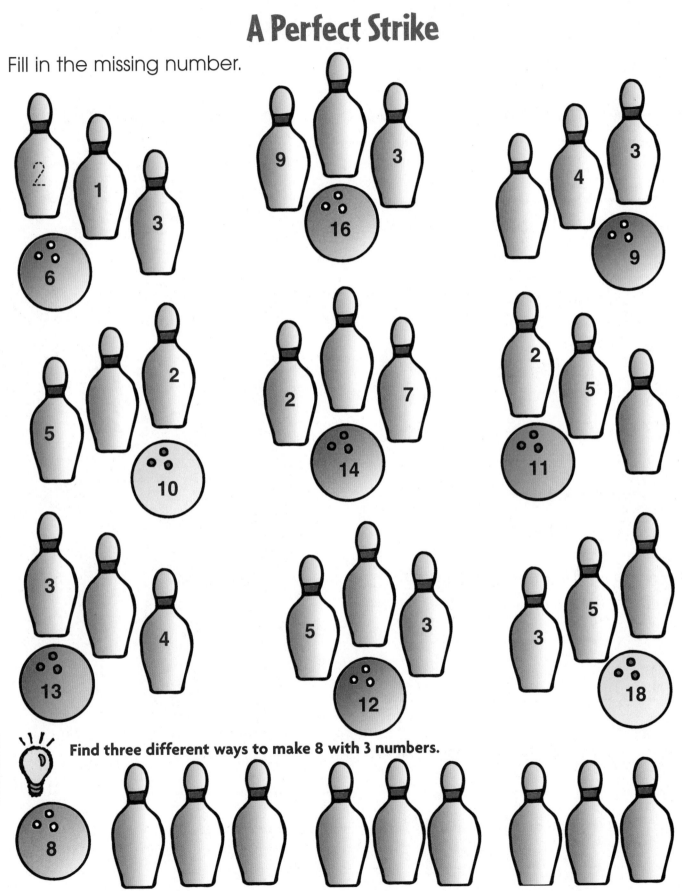

Find three different ways to make 8 with 3 numbers.

What a Treat!

Find the number in the mouse and cheese. ☐

Find the sum of the numbers in the cheese.

_____ + _____ + _____ = _____

Find the sum of the numbers in the mouse.

_____ + _____ + _____ = _____

Find the number in the
rabbit and carrot. ☐

Find the sum of the largest number in the
rabbit and the smallest number in the carrot.

_____ + _____ = _____

Find the difference between the largest
and smallest number in the carrot.

_____ - _____ = _____

 Find the sum of all the numbers in the mouse and cheese.

_____ + _____ + _____ + _____ + _____ = _____

Find the sum of all the numbers in the rabbit and carrot.

_____ + _____ + _____ + _____ + _____ = _____

Have a Heart

Circle a group of 10. Write the number of tens and ones.

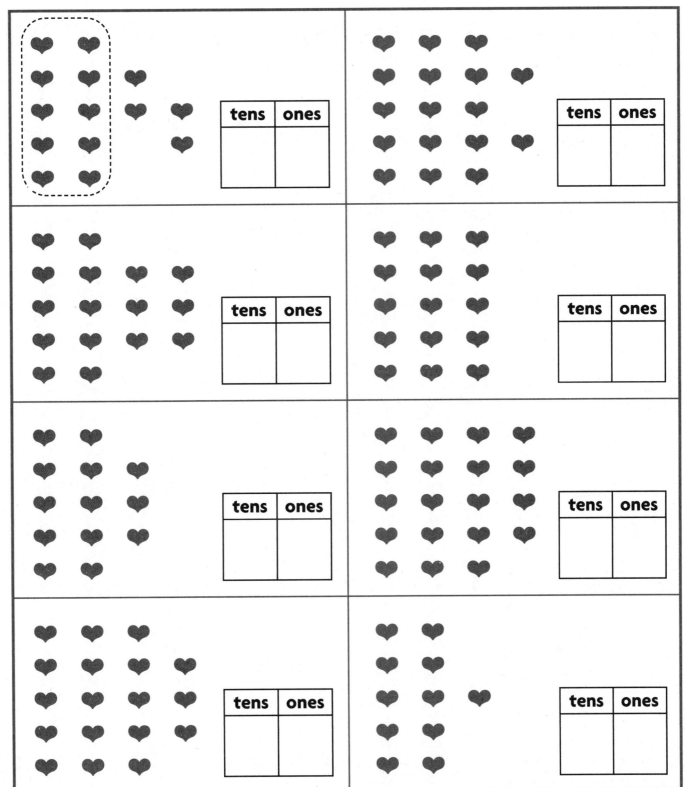

tens	ones

tens	ones

tens	ones

tens	ones

tens	ones

tens	ones

tens	ones

tens	ones

Beautiful Butterflies

Add. Color the picture using the color code.

Color Code

26	red
29	orange
38	green
54	purple
87	yellow

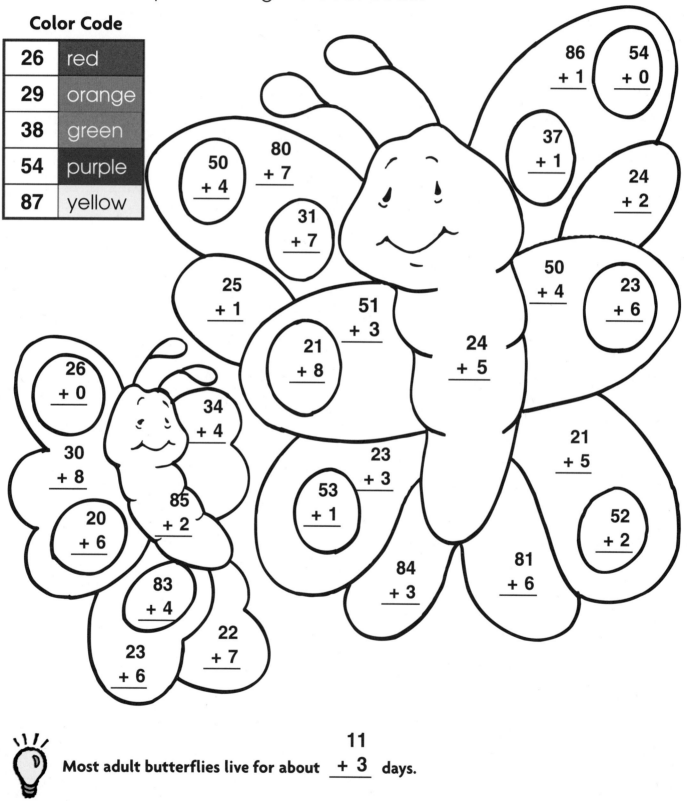

Most adult butterflies live for about
$$\begin{array}{r} 11 \\ +\ 3 \\ \hline \end{array}$$ days.

Where's the Beach?

Add. To find the path to the beach, color each box with an odd answer yellow.

14 + 3	34 + 2	81 + 3

76 + 2	25 + 4	56 + 3	11 + 3	40 + 8
87 + 1	22 + 2	32 + 3	65 + 1	93 + 5
10 + 8	41 + 2	70 + 7	32 + 6	84 + 4
73 + 5	63 + 2	55 + 1	41 + 5	23 + 3

98 + 1	53 + 4	82 + 5

© Scholastic Inc.

By the Seashore

Use the code below to write each missing number. Add.

93
+ _____
_____

82
+ _____
_____

14
+ _____
_____

21
+ _____
_____

53
+ _____
_____

45
+ _____
_____

73
+ _____
_____

36
+ _____
_____

61
+ _____
_____

32
+ _____
_____

Find the sum for all the shells. _____ + _____ + _____ + _____ + _____ = _____

Sail Away

Finish each addition sentence. Add.

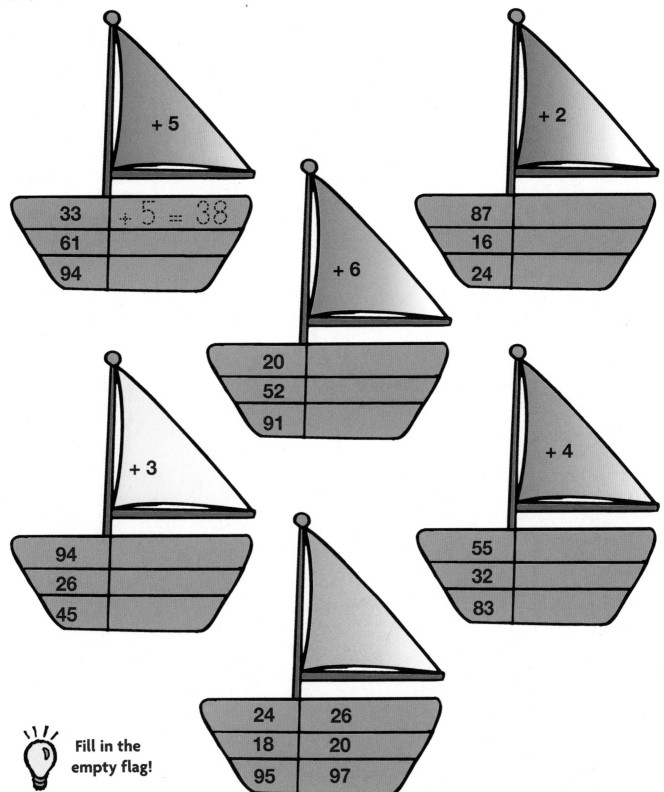

+ 5

33	+ 5 = 38
61	
94	

+ 2

87	
16	
24	

+ 6

20	
52	
91	

+ 3

94	
26	
45	

+ 4

55	
32	
83	

24	26
18	20
95	97

**Fill in the
empty flag!**

Dino-Math

Subtract. Color the picture using the color code.

Color Code

16	red
22	orange
34	purple
57	blue
73	yellow
85	green

87
− 2

89
− 4

27
− 5

19
− 3

88
− 3

39
− 5

34
− 0

86
− 1

85
− 0

78
− 5

58
− 1

28
− 6

77
− 4

38
− 4

29
− 7

35
− 1

Number Buddies

Subtract. Remember: the largest number always goes on top!

A. 7   39   39 − 7

B. 1   54

C. 87   6

D. 3   73

E. 25   4

F. 2   42

G. 7   98

H. 66   5

💡 **Fill in each missing number.**

39   35

27   20

88   83

Treasure Island

Subtract.

43 − 1	95 − 5	79 − 3	36 − 4	89 − 7	66 − 3	83 − 2
59 − 9	37 − 2	24 − 3	27 − 6	42 − 1	90 − 0	55 − 2
33 − 3	84 − 4	28 − 8	71 − 1	62 − 2	68 − 3	77 − 3

Use the clues to find the gold, the ship, and the treasure in the
boxes above.

 **Find the
gold.**

The difference is
greater than **50** and
less than **55**. Color
the box with the
gold yellow.

 **Find the
ship.**

The difference is greater than **30** and less than
35. Color the box with the ship orange.

 **Find
the sunken
treasure.**

The difference is greater than **70** and less than
75. Color the box with the treasure red.

© Scholastic Inc.

Riding on Air

Add. Color the picture using the color code.

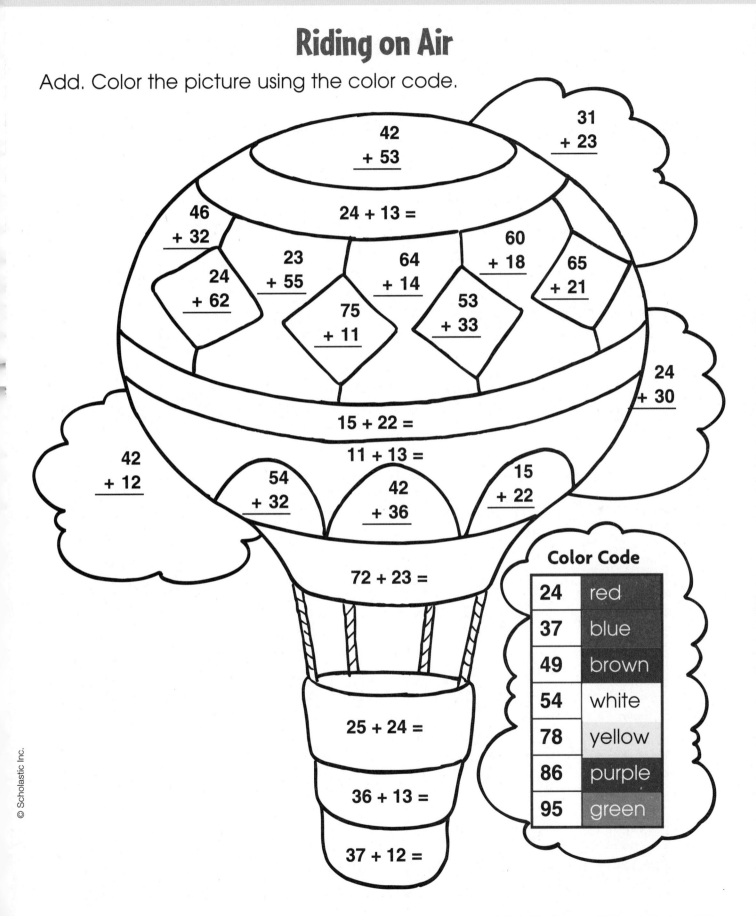

Color Code

24	red
37	blue
49	brown
54	white
78	yellow
86	purple
95	green

$$42 + 53$$
$$31 + 23$$
$$46 + 32$$
$$24 + 13 =$$
$$23 + 55$$
$$24 + 62$$
$$64 + 14$$
$$60 + 18$$
$$65 + 21$$
$$75 + 11$$
$$53 + 33$$
$$24 + 30$$
$$15 + 22 =$$
$$11 + 13 =$$
$$42 + 12$$
$$54 + 32$$
$$42 + 36$$
$$15 + 22$$
$$72 + 23 =$$
$$25 + 24 =$$
$$36 + 13 =$$
$$37 + 12 =$$

© Scholastic Inc.

Number Puzzler

Can you spell 80 in two letters?

To find out how, do the addition problems. If the answer is even, shade the square. If your answers are correct, the shaded squares will spell the answer.

12 + 13	24 + 34	22 + 21	77 + 22	35 + 43	52 + 12	40 + 52
11 + 31	30 + 39	46 + 52	15 + 12	10 + 71	63 + 11	13 + 80
36 + 32	30 + 10	11 + 11	15 + 4	20 + 21	15 + 11	22 + 33
14 + 14	13 + 16	10 + 20	14 + 25	11 + 20	15 + 21	20 + 31
36 + 52	21 + 32	10 + 50	44 + 41	24 + 43	31 + 21	13 + 82

Color the Sunflower

Do the addition problems in the sunflower picture below. Then use the Color Key to tell you what color to make each answer.

Extra: Write your age on four flashcards, and then add a 6, 7, 8, and 9 to each of the cards. Practice the answers with a friend.

Color Key
56 = green
68 = orange
89 = yellow
97 = blue

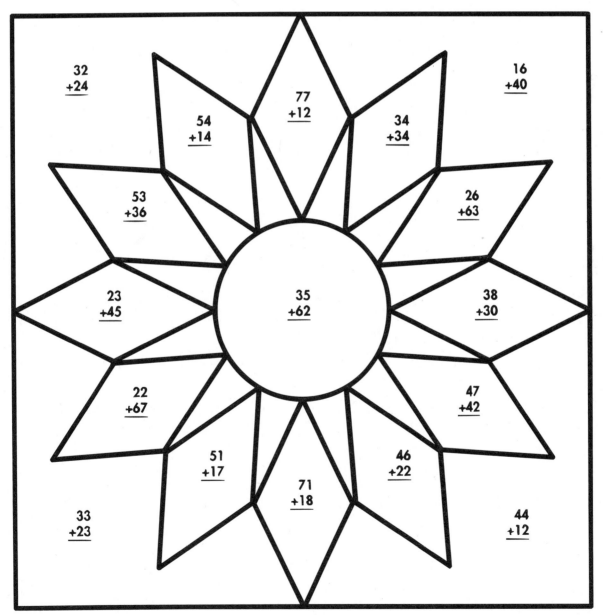

Roger the Rooster

Why did Roger the Rooster decide not to get in a barnyard fight?

To find out, add the numbers and shade the blocks as described below.

Shade the squares in row 1 that contain answers less than 25.

Shade the squares in row 2 that contain odd-numbered answers.

Shade the squares in row 3 that contain answers greater than 35.

Shade the squares in row 4 that contain even-numbered answers.

Shade the squares in row 5 that contain answers that end in zero.

13 + 11 **H**	26 + 33 **Y**	16 + 31 **O**	10 + 12 **E**	64 + 24 **U**
20 + 15 **W**	71 + 12 **A**	25 + 21 **W**	51 + 10 **S**	22 + 16 **O**
22 + 10 **L**	14 + 14 **C**	20 + 10 **E**	25 + 31 **A**	21 + 3 **L**
42 + 30 **C**	13 + 43 **H**	54 + 15 **F**	21 + 61 **I**	61 + 33 **C**
10 + 30 **K**	20 + 30 **E**	16 + 32 **J**	71 + 23 **S**	70 + 20 **N**

Baseball Puzzle

What animal can always be found at a baseball game?

To find out, do the subtraction problems. If the answer is greater than 9, color the shapes black. If the answer is less than 10, color the shapes red.

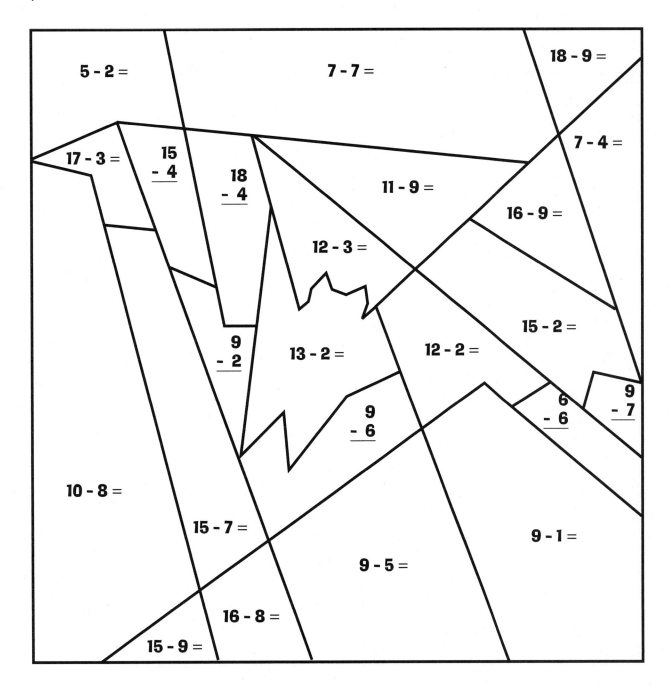

© Scholastic Inc.

Color the Bowtie

Do the subtraction problems in the picture below. Then use the Color Key to tell you what color to make each answer.

Extra: On the back of this sheet of paper, draw a picture of four of your friends or family members. Give each one a bowtie!

Color Key

14 = red

26 = purple

33 = blue

47 = yellow

63 = green

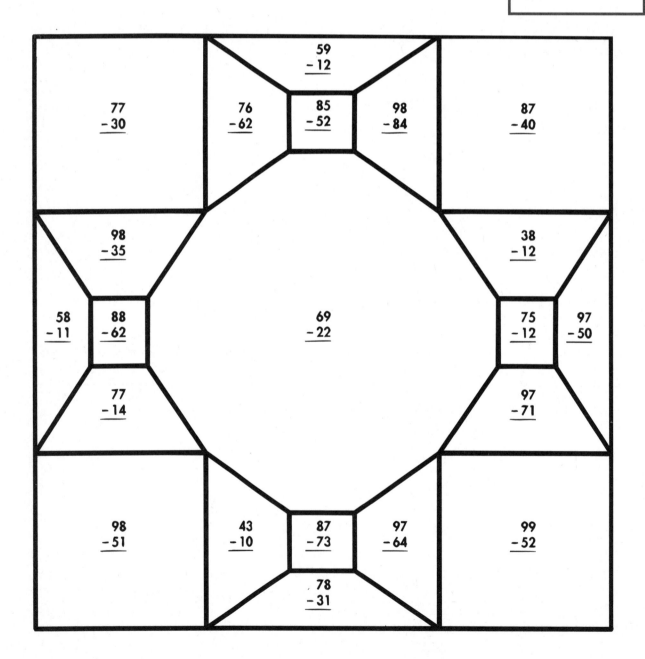

Detective Work

Use the code to help Detective Dave discover the secret phone number. The first problem has been done for you.

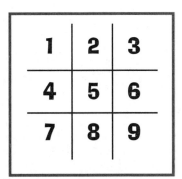

1.

$$7 - 1 = 6$$

2.

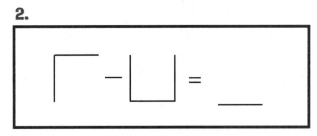

3.

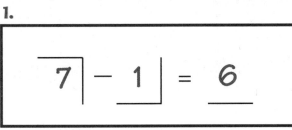

4.

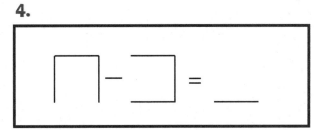

5.

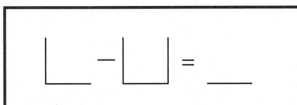

6.

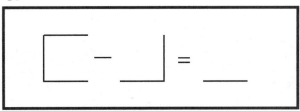

7.

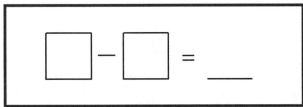

The phone number is:

_ _ _ - _ _ _ _

© Scholastic Inc.

Have a Ball

Subtract.

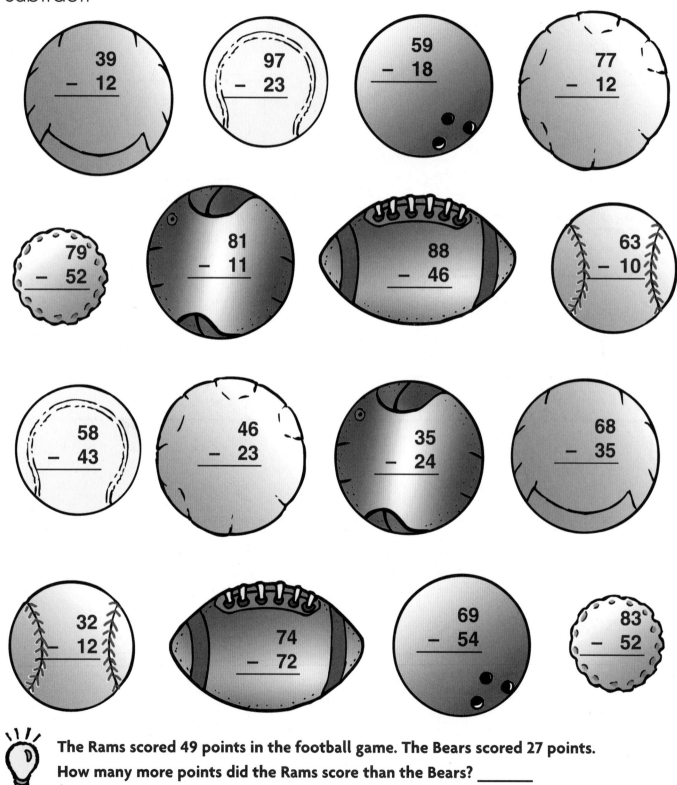

39
− 12

97
− 23

59
− 18

77
− 12

79
− 52

81
− 11

88
− 46

63
− 10

58
− 43

46
− 23

35
− 24

68
− 35

32
− 12

74
− 72

69
− 54

83
− 52

The Rams scored 49 points in the football game. The Bears scored 27 points.
How many more points did the Rams score than the Bears? _____

Opposites Attract

Add or subtract. Connect the magnets that have the same answer.

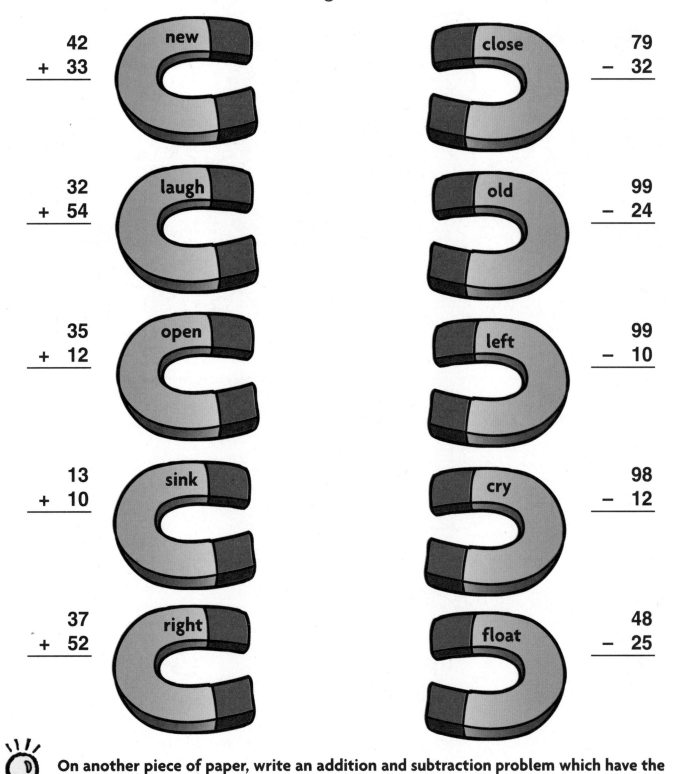

42 + 33 — new	close — 79 − 32
32 + 54 — laugh	old — 99 − 24
35 + 12 — open	left — 99 − 10
13 + 10 — sink	cry — 98 − 12
37 + 52 — right	float — 48 − 25

On another piece of paper, write an addition and subtraction problem which have the same answer.

How Much Money?

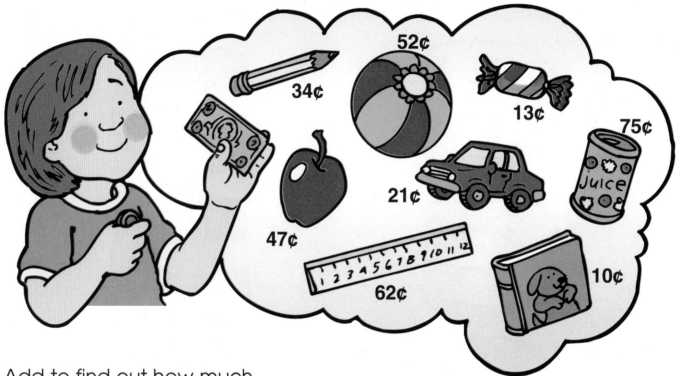

Add to find out how much.

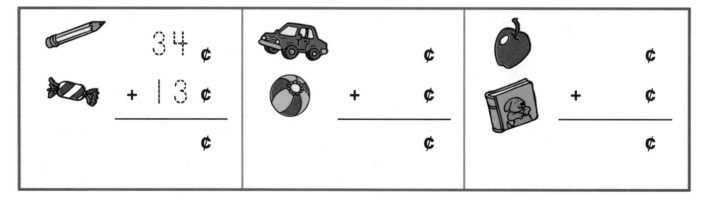

3 4 ¢ + 1 3 ¢ ———— ¢	___ ¢ + ___ ¢ ———— ___ ¢	___ ¢ + ___ ¢ ———— ___ ¢

Subtract to find out how much.

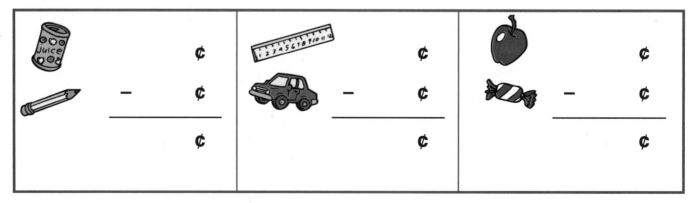

___ ¢ – ___ ¢ ———— ___ ¢	___ ¢ – ___ ¢ ———— ___ ¢	___ ¢ – ___ ¢ ———— ___ ¢

Snuggle Up With a Book

Day of the Week	Reading Minutes
Sunday	97
Monday	28
Tuesday	73
Wednesday	44
Thursday	51
Friday	45
Saturday	80

Use the chart to answer the questions.

A. What day did Alex read for the longest time?

_____

B. How many minutes did Alex read on Wednesday and Friday? _____ minutes

C. What day did Alex read for the shortest time?

_____

D. How many more minutes did Alex read on Sunday than Tuesday? _____ minutes

E. How many minutes did Alex read on Monday and Thursday? _____ minutes

F. How many more minutes did Alex read on Tuesday than Thursday? _____ minutes

 One hour is 60 minutes. On what days did Alex read longer than one hour?

_____, _____, _____

Let the Sun Shine

Add or subtract. Then use the code to fill in the letters to finish each sun fact.

13	26	34	42	57	63	71	76	85	88
f	a	s	g	r	e	l	h	t	i

$$13 + 21 \qquad 32 + 53 \qquad 57 - 31 \qquad 89 - 32$$

____ ____ ____ ____

The sun is a ____ ____ ____ ____.

$$30 + 41 \qquad 98 - 10 \qquad 12 + 30 \qquad 97 - 21 \qquad 99 - 14$$

____ ____ ____ ____ ____

The sun gives ____ ____ ____ ____ ____ and

$$34 + 42 \qquad 51 + 12 \qquad 88 - 62 \qquad 42 + 43$$

____ ____ ____ ____

____ ____ ____ ____ to Earth.

$$88 - 17 \qquad 56 + 32 \qquad 49 - 36 \qquad 30 + 33$$

____ ____ ____ ____

Without the sun, there would be no ____ ____ ____ ____.

Animal Surprises

Add or subtract. Match the answer to the animal fact.

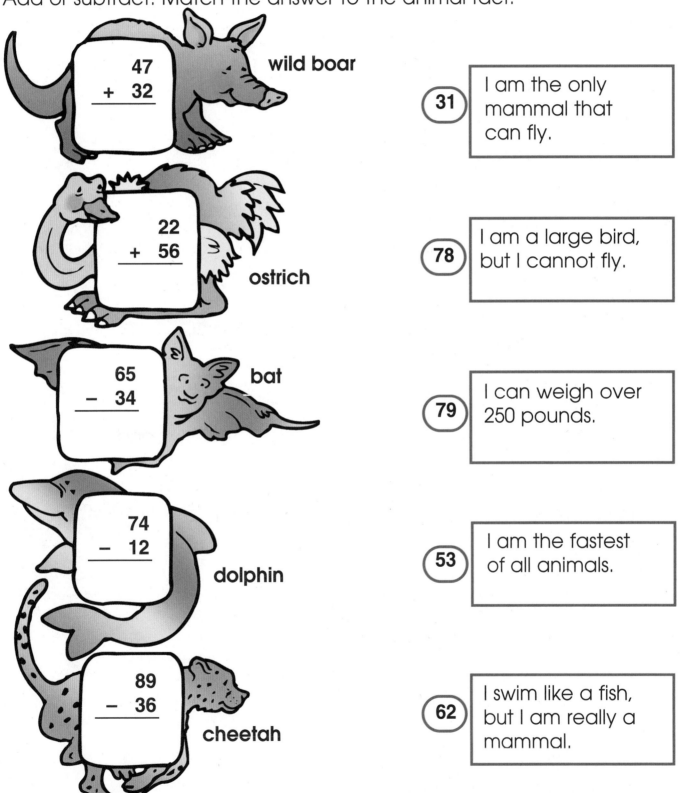

wild boar

$$\begin{array}{r} 47 \\ + \ 32 \\ \hline \end{array}$$

ostrich

$$\begin{array}{r} 22 \\ + \ 56 \\ \hline \end{array}$$

bat

$$\begin{array}{r} 65 \\ - \ 34 \\ \hline \end{array}$$

dolphin

$$\begin{array}{r} 74 \\ - \ 12 \\ \hline \end{array}$$

cheetah

$$\begin{array}{r} 89 \\ - \ 36 \\ \hline \end{array}$$

31 I am the only mammal that can fly.

78 I am a large bird, but I cannot fly.

79 I can weigh over 250 pounds.

53 I am the fastest of all animals.

62 I swim like a fish, but I am really a mammal.

© Scholastic Inc.

Fishbowl Families

Add or subtract. Circle the fish that
does not belong with the family.
Hint: Look at the tens place.

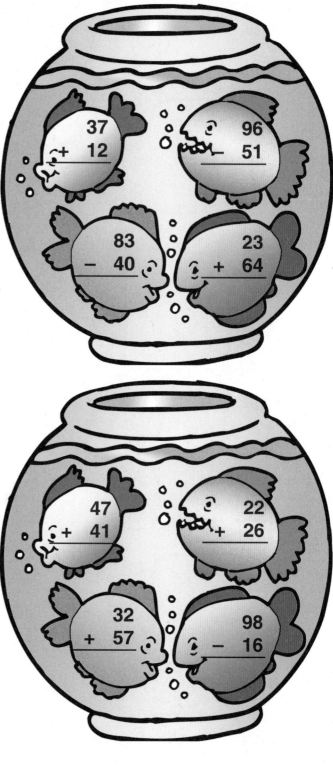

$$37 + 12$$

$$96 - 51$$

$$83 - 40$$

$$23 + 64$$

$$42 + 23$$

$$33 + 36$$

$$27 + 12$$

$$51 + 13$$

$$47 + 41$$

$$22 + 26$$

$$32 + 57$$

$$98 - 16$$

**Make another family with 7 in the
tens place.**

Scholastic Success With
MATH

Color the Basket

Count the number of dots or triangles in each shape. Then use the Color Key to tell you what color to make each shape. (For example, a shape with 7 dots will be colored green.)

Extra: On the back of this sheet of paper, draw a basket filled with six things you would carry in it.

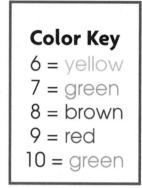

Color Key
6 = yellow
7 = green
8 = brown
9 = red
10 = green

Number User

I use numbers to tell about myself.

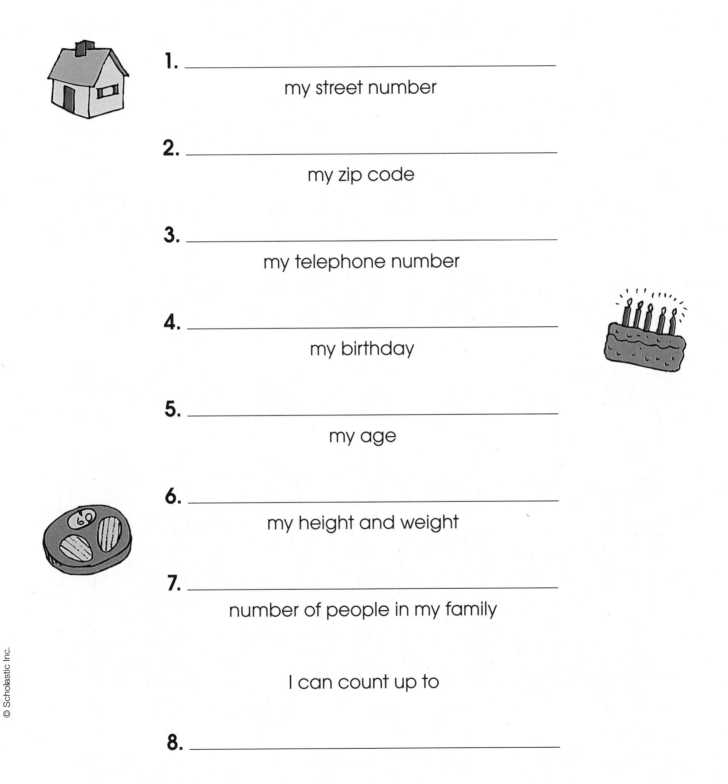

1. _____
my street number

2. _____
my zip code

3. _____
my telephone number

4. _____
my birthday

5. _____
my age

6. _____
my height and weight

7. _____
number of people in my family

I can count up to

8. _____

Frog School

At Frog School, Croaker Frog and his friends sit on lily pads.

Are there enough lily pads for all the frogs in Croaker's class?
Yes _____   No _____

Draw lines to match the frogs with the lily pads.

How many frogs need lily pads? _____ .

Odd and Even Patterns

A pattern can have two things repeating. This is called an "AB"
pattern.

1. Look around the classroom. What "AB" patterns do you see?
   Draw one "AB" pattern in the box.

2. Use red and blue crayons to color the numbers in the chart using an
   "AB" pattern.

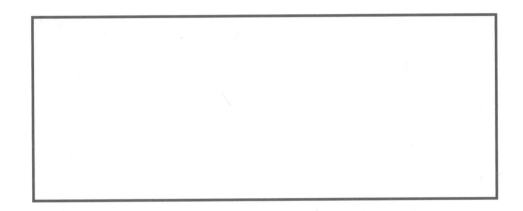

Hundred's Chart

1	2	3	4	5	6	7	8	9	10
11	12	13	14	15	16	17	18	19	20
21	22	23	24	25	26	27	28	29	30
31	32	33	34	35	36	37	38	39	40
41	42	43	44	45	46	47	48	49	50
51	52	53	54	55	56	57	58	59	60
61	62	63	64	65	66	67	68	69	70
71	72	73	74	75	76	77	78	79	80
81	82	83	84	85	86	87	88	89	90
91	92	93	94	95	96	97	98	99	100

Use this rule:
  1 = red
  2 = blue
  3 = red
  4 = blue, and so on

The blue numbers are
even numbers. They can
be split evenly into 2
whole numbers.

The red numbers are **odd
numbers**. They cannot be
split evenly into 2 whole
numbers.

Classroom Garage Sale

Tolu's class did some spring cleaning. Then they had a garage sale. They sorted the things they were selling. Sort these objects into like groups. Draw the items of each group on one of the tables below.

Below each table, write a label for the group.

Flowers in a Pot

Count the dots in the boxes. Then color the matching number word.

green   yellow

red   purple

blue

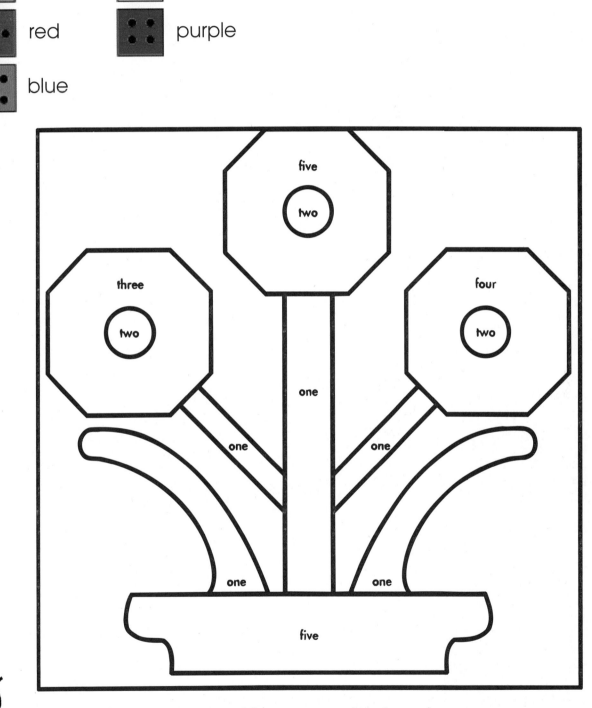

Use bright colors to draw a pot of flowers on another sheet of paper.

Sign Shape

Street signs come in different shapes. Use string to form the shapes below. Work with a partner. Answer the questions below about the shapes, too.

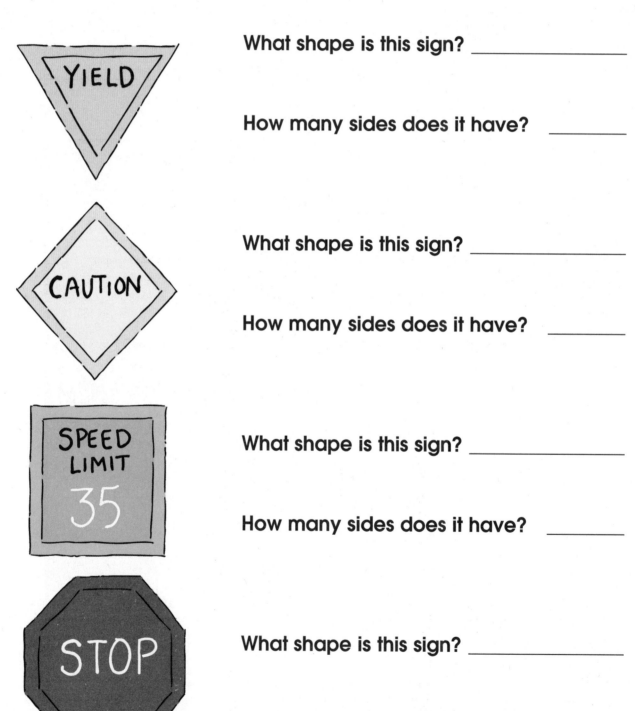

What shape is this sign? _____

How many sides does it have? _____

What shape is this sign? _____

How many sides does it have? _____

What shape is this sign? _____

How many sides does it have? _____

What shape is this sign? _____

How many sides does it have? _____

Bird Feeder Geometry

It's spring! The birds are coming back. Kwaku and his mother made two bird feeders.

What shapes can you find on their feeders? Write your ideas on

the lines. _____

_____

Shape Study

"Symmetry" exists when the two halves of something are mirror images of each other.

Look at the pictures below. Color those that show symmetry.
(Hint: Imagine the pictures are folded on the dotted lines.)

Complete the drawings below. Connect the dots to show the other half. (Hint: The pictures are symmetrical!)

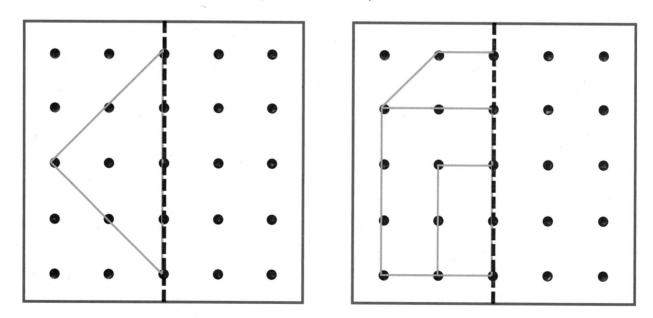

Picking Out Patterns

On the 100th day of school, everyone in Pat's class picked out patterns on the 100 Chart. Look at the chart below.

1	2	3	4	5	6	7	8	9	10
11	12	13	14	15	16	17	18	19	20
21	22	23	24	25	26	27	28	29	30
31	32	33	34	35	36	37	38	39	40
41	42	43	44	45	46	47	48	49	50
51	52	53	54	55	56	57	58	59	60
61	62	63	64	65	66	67	68	69	70
71	72	73	74	75	76	77	78	79	80
81	82	83	84	85	86	87	88	89	90
91	92	93	94	95	96	97	98	99	100

Find and finish the pattern starting with 2, 12, 22

_____

Find and finish the pattern starting with 100, 90, 80

_____

Find and finish the pattern starting with 97, 87, 77

_____

Find and finish the pattern starting with 11, 22, 33

_____

Mystery Critter

I climb up the side of walls and never fall.

I am a fast runner and have a very long tail. Who am I? _____

To find out, connect the numbers in order from 20 to 68.

Snowflakes on Mittens

Estimate how many snowflakes are on each mitten.
For the first mitten, skip count by 2s to find out.
(You can circle groups of 2.)
For the second mitten, skip count by 5s to check your answer.
(You can circle groups of 5.)

Would snowflakes really wait for you to count?

Explain your answer:

Patterns of Five

Look at the number chart below. Starting with 1, count 5 squares. Color in the fifth square. Then count 5 more squares and color in the fifth square. Keep going until you reach 100.

Hundred's Chart

1	2	3	4	5	6	7	8	9	10
11	12	13	14	15	16	17	18	19	20
21	22	23	24	25	26	27	28	29	30
31	32	33	34	35	36	37	38	39	40
41	42	43	44	45	46	47	48	49	50
51	52	53	54	55	56	57	58	59	60
61	62	63	64	65	66	67	68	69	70
71	72	73	74	75	76	77	78	79	80
81	82	83	84	85	86	87	88	89	90
91	92	93	94	95	96	97	98	99	100

Tally marks can be arranged in groups of five, like this: ЦНТ ЦНТ ЦНТ
Then you can count by fives.

Count how many girls and boys are in your class. Draw tally marks in groups of five.

Girls: _____   Boys: _____

Now count the total number. Write the totals here:

Girls: _____   Boys: _____

Tentacles and Legs

Finish the ocean animals.
Then complete each number sentence.

Draw tentacles so each jellyfish has 5.

3 + ___ = 5   4 + ___ = 5

Draw arms so each octopus has 8.

5 + ___ = 8   2 + ___ = 8

Draw legs so each crab has 6.

2 + ___ = 6   3 + ___ = 6

Ladybug Dots

Every year, ladybugs hibernate when the weather gets cool. Count the dots on each ladybug wing. Then write an equation to show the total number of dots each ladybug has. The first one has been done for you.

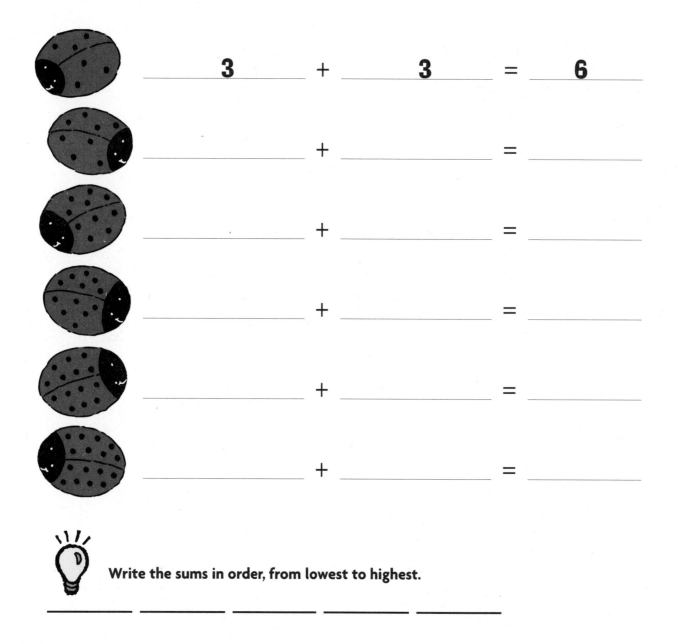

$$3 + 3 = 6$$

$$\_\_\_ + \_\_\_ = \_\_\_$$

$$\_\_\_ + \_\_\_ = \_\_\_$$

$$\_\_\_ + \_\_\_ = \_\_\_$$

$$\_\_\_ + \_\_\_ = \_\_\_$$

$$\_\_\_ + \_\_\_ = \_\_\_$$

Write the sums in order, from lowest to highest.

____ ____ ____ ____ ____

What pattern do you see?

_____

Pattern Block Design

How many total pieces are in this pattern block design?

2 + 2 + 1= _____

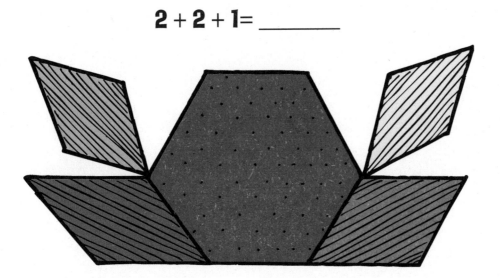

Now make your own design by drawing 5 pattern blocks. Connect the blocks to form a pattern different from the one above. You may want to use a block pattern more than once.

Write an equation to show how many of each shape you used.

Equation: _____

Coin-Toss Subtraction

Toss 3 coins. Write "H" for heads or "T" for tails in the circles below to show how the coins landed. Then finish each sentence to tell about your toss. Write a subtraction equation to show your toss, too. Write the number of heads first. We did the first one for you. Try it three times.

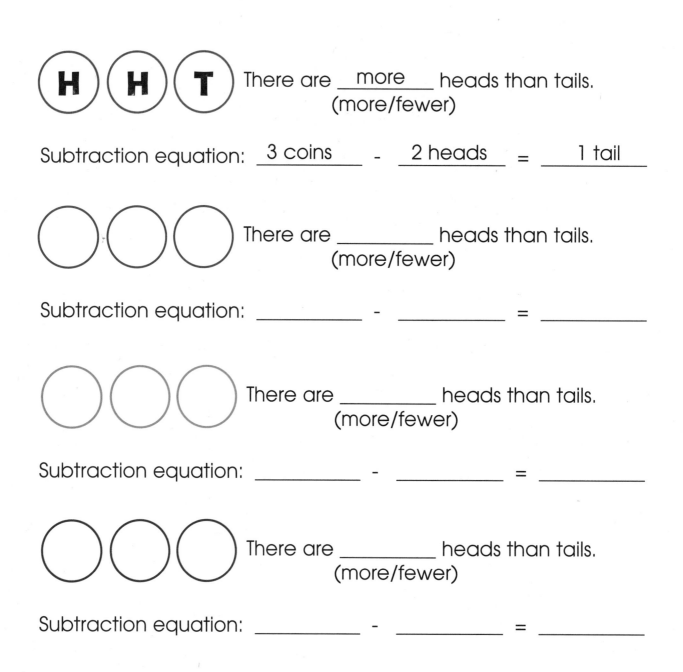

There are ___more___ heads than tails.
(more/fewer)

Subtraction equation: __3 coins__ - __2 heads__ = __1 tail__

There are _____ heads than tails.
(more/fewer)

Subtraction equation: _____ - _____ = _____

There are _____ heads than tails.
(more/fewer)

Subtraction equation: _____ - _____ = _____

There are _____ heads than tails.
(more/fewer)

Subtraction equation: _____ - _____ = _____

What's Your Story?

Look at the equation below.

3 + 3 = 6

Make up a story to go with the equation.

Draw a picture in the box to go with your story.

Now write about your picture on the lines below.

_____

_____

_____

_____

_____

Coin-Toss Addition

Toss 6 coins. Write "H" for heads or "T" for tails in the circles below to show your toss. Then write the addition equation. Write the number of "heads" first. We did the first one for you. Try it five times.

(H)(H)(H)(H)(T)(T) Equation: ___$4 + 2 = 6$___

◯◯◯◯◯◯ Equation: _____

◯◯◯◯◯◯ Equation: _____

◯◯◯◯◯◯ Equation: _____

◯◯◯◯◯◯ Equation: _____

◯◯◯◯◯◯ Equation: _____

© Scholastic Inc.

Time to Get Up!

Twenty animals were hibernating near Sleepy Pond.
5 of them woke up. Color 5 animals below.

How many are still sleeping? _____

A week later, 7 more woke up. Color 7 other animals.

How many are still sleeping? _____

Money Matters

Alex asked his little brother Billy to trade piggy banks.

Alex's bank has these coins: Billy's has these coins:

Do you think this is a fair trade? _____

Test your answer:

Add up Alex's coins: _____

Add up Billy's coins: _____

Write the totals in this Greater Than/Less Than equation:

_____ > _____

Who has more money? _____

The Truth About the Tooth Fairy

Look at Ali Gator's teeth.

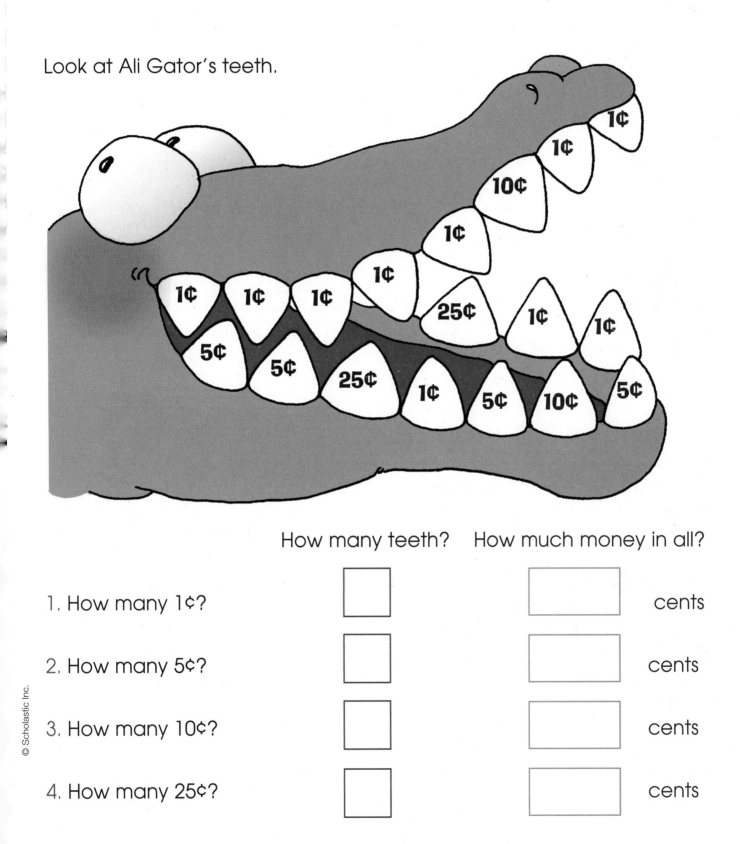

	How many teeth?	How much money in all?
1. How many 1¢?		cents
2. How many 5¢?		cents
3. How many 10¢?		cents
4. How many 25¢?		cents

Measuring Up

People didn't always measure with rulers. Long ago, Egyptians and other peoples measured objects with body parts. Try it!

A "digit" is the width of your middle finger at the top joint where it bends.

How many digits long is:

a pair of scissors? _____

a math book? _____

a crayon? _____

A "palm" is the width of your palm.

How many palms long is:

a telephone book? _____

your desk? _____

a ruler? _____

A "span" is the length from the tip of your pinkie to the tip of your thumb when your hand is wide open.

How many spans long is:

a broom handle? _____

a table? _____

a door? _____

© Scholastic Inc.

Penguin Family on Parade

The penguin family is part of the winter parade. They need to line up from shortest to tallest. Give them a hand! Use a ruler to measure each penguin. Label each penguin with its height. Then write the name of each penguin in size order, from smallest to tallest.

Paul
Height:

_____

inches

Peter
Height:

_____

inches

Patty
Height:

_____

inches

Petunia
Height:

_____

inches

Size Order:

_____   _____   _____   _____

(smallest)   (tallest)

Look and Learn

Look at each picture. Estimate how long you think it is. Then measure each picture with a ruler. Write the actual length in inches.

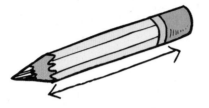

Estimate: _____ inches
Actual: _____ inches

Estimate: _____ inches
Actual: _____ inches

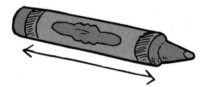

Estimate: _____ inches
Actual: _____ inches

Estimate: _____ inches
Actual: _____ inches

 Practice measuring other things in the room with a ruler.

Turn Up the Volume

How many quarts equal 1 gallon? Find out! Fill a quart container with water. Pour it into a gallon container. Keep doing it until the gallon is full. Color the correct number of quarts below. Write the numeral on the line: **1 gallon = _____ quarts.**

Now try it with other containers, too.

1 quart = _____ pints

1 pint = _____ cups

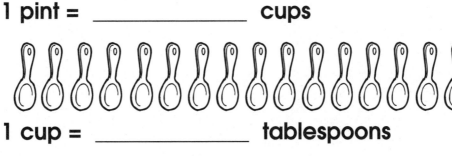

1 cup = _____ tablespoons

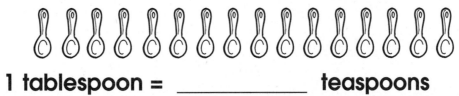

1 tablespoon = _____ teaspoons

Adding Sides

Use the inch side of a ruler and measure each side of each rectangle. Write the inches in the spaces below. Then add up all the sides to find the perimeter, or distance, around each rectangle.

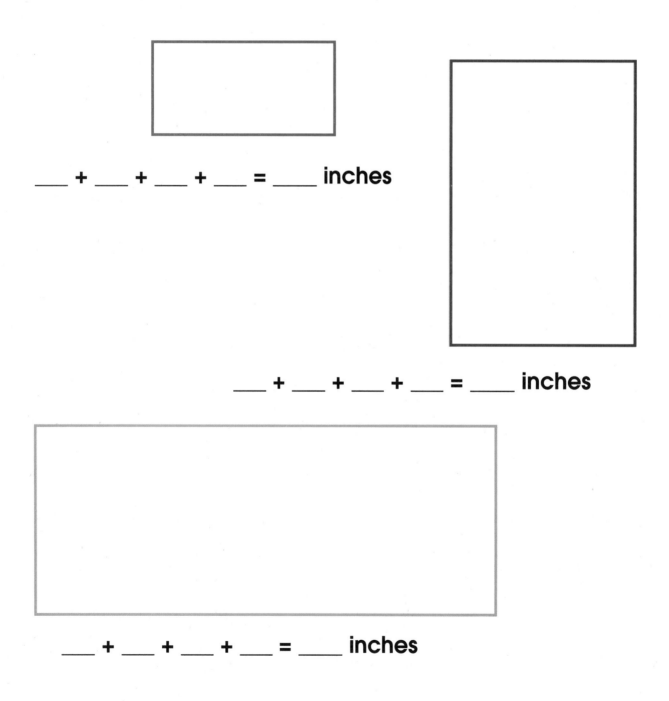

___ + ___ + ___ + ___ = ____ inches

___ + ___ + ___ + ___ = ____ inches

___ + ___ + ___ + ___ = ____ inches

Centimeters

Things can be measured using centimeters. Get a ruler that measures in centimeters. Measure the pictures of the objects below.

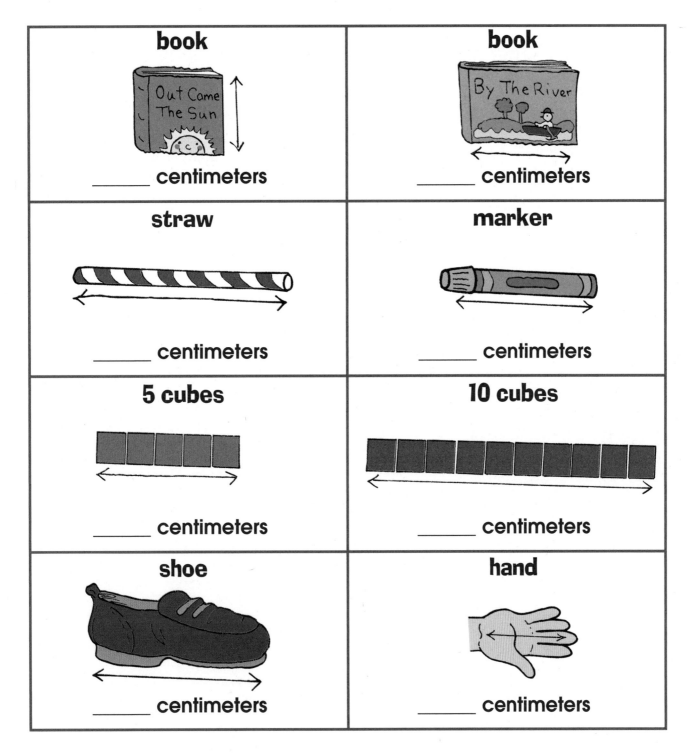

book

_____ centimeters

book

_____ centimeters

straw

_____ centimeters

marker

_____ centimeters

5 cubes

_____ centimeters

10 cubes

_____ centimeters

shoe

_____ centimeters

hand

_____ centimeters

Five Senses

We learn about the world by using our 5 senses. The 5 senses are seeing, hearing, smelling, touching, and tasting.

Look at the pictures on the left side of the graph. Think about which of your senses you use to learn about it. Draw a checkmark in the box to show the senses used. (Hint: You might use more than one.)

	See	Hear	Smell	Touch	Taste
🐓					
☀					
🥤					
🌸					
🥁					

Now graph how many senses you used for each object.

Rainbow Graph

Which color of the rainbow is your favorite? Color in the box for your favorite color. Have 5 classmates color the boxes to show their favorite colors, too.

Which color is liked the most? _____

Which color is liked the least? _____

Are any colors tied? _____

Which ones? _____

Violet

Blue

Green

Yellow

Orange

Red

School Supplies

1. Find each letter and

   number pair on the graph.

2. Color a yellow square

   for each pair.

3. What picture did you make?

_____

	Across	Up			Across	Up
1.	C	4		8.	F	5
2.	C	5		9.	G	4
3.	D	4		10.	G	5
4.	D	5		11.	H	4
5.	E	4		12.	H	5
6.	E	5		13.	I	4
7.	F	4		14.	I	5

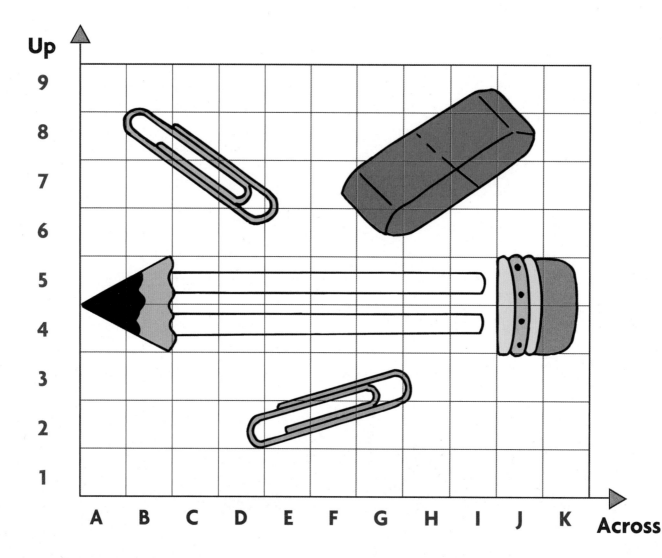

Surprises!

1. Find each number pair on the graph. Make a dot for each.

2. Connect the dots in the order that you make them.

3. What picture did you make?

_____

	Across	Up
1.	9	2
2.	7	4
3.	8	4
4.	6	6
5.	7	6
6.	5	8
7.	3	6
8.	4	6
9.	2	4
10.	3	4
11.	1	2

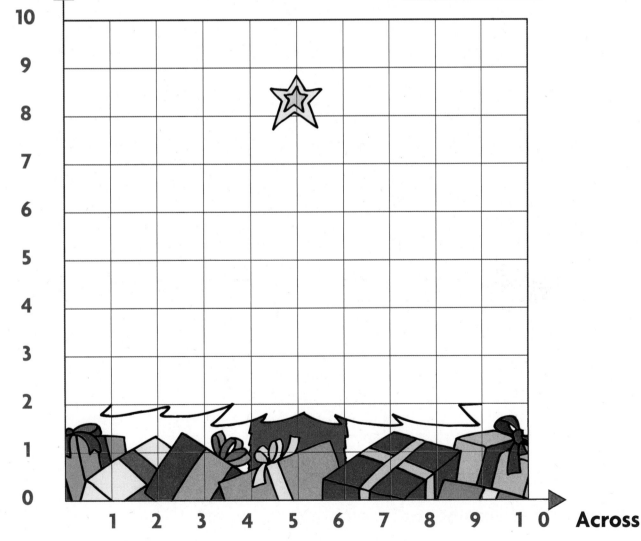

December Weather

In December, Mrs. Monroe's class drew the weather on a calendar. Each kind of weather has a picture:

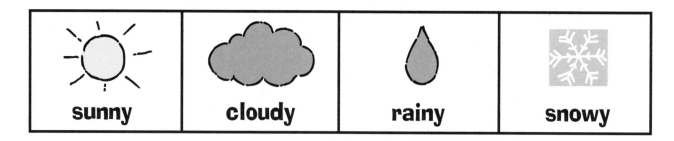

| sunny | cloudy | rainy | snowy |

Look at the calendar. Answer the questions below.

How many sunny days did they have? _____

How many cloudy days did they have? _____

How many rainy days did they have? _____

How many snowy days did they have? _____

Which kind of weather did they have the most? _____

Fun With Fractions

A fraction is a part of a whole.

The shapes below are split into parts, or fractions.
Color only the shapes that are split into equal parts (equal fractions).

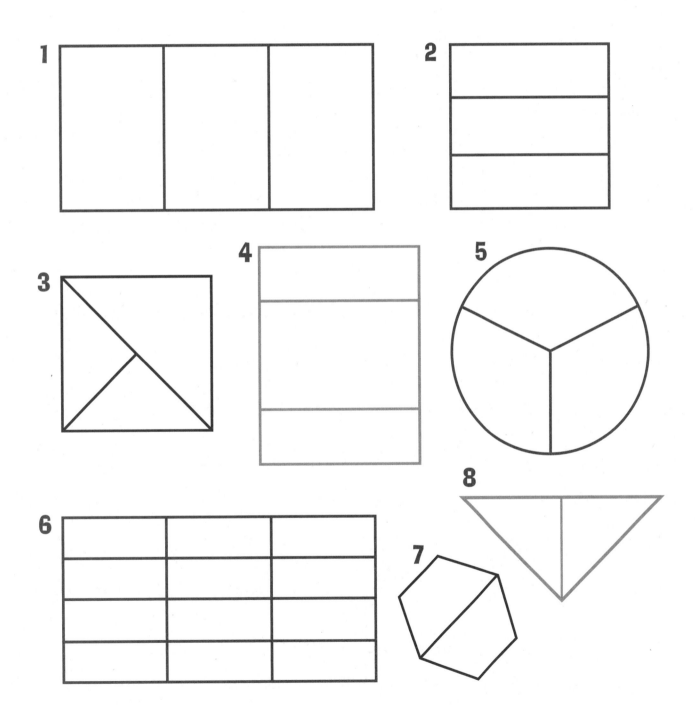

© Scholastic Inc.

Parts to Color

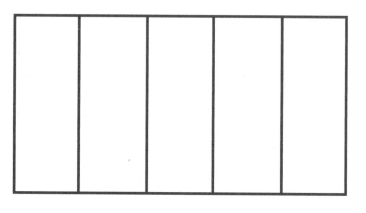

A fraction has two numbers. The top number will tell you how many parts to color. The bottom number tells you how many parts there are.

Color 1/5 of the circle.   Color 4/5 of the rectangle.

Color 3/5 of the ants.   Color 2/5 of the spiders.

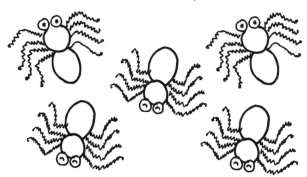

Color 0/5 of the bees.   Color 5/5 of the worms.

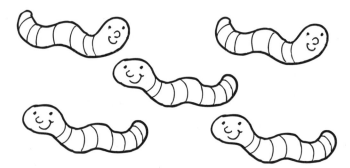

More Parts to Color

A fraction has two numbers. The top number will tell you how many parts to color. The bottom number tells you how many parts there are.

Color 1/8 of the circle.   Color 6/8 of the rectangle.

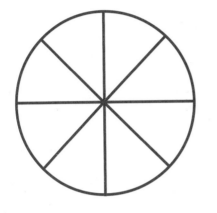
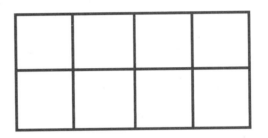

Color 4/8 of the suns.   Color 8/8 of the stars.

Color 2/8 of the moons.   Color 3/8 of the planets.

Clock Work

Draw the hands on the clock so it shows 2:00.

Draw the hands on the clock so it shows 3:00.

Draw the hands on the clock so it shows 4:00.

Draw the hands on the clock so it shows 5:00.

What do you do at 2:00 in the afternoon?

Write about it on the lines below.

_____

_____

More Clock Work

Draw the hands on the clock so it shows 3:00.

Draw the hands on the clock so it shows 6:00.

Draw the hands on the clock so it shows 9:00.

Draw the hands on the clock so it shows 12:00.

What do you do at 3:00 in the afternoon?

Write about it on the lines below.

_____

_____

Even More Clock Work

Draw the hands on the clock so it shows 4:00.

Draw the hands on the clock so it shows 4:30.

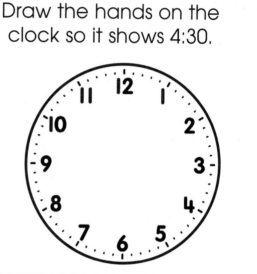

What do you do at 4:00 in the afternoon?

Write about it on the line below.

_____

Draw the hands on the clock so it shows 6:00.

Draw the hands on the clock so it shows 6:30.

What do you do at 6:00 in the evening?

Write about it on the line below.

_____

About Time

Why do we need to know how to tell time? List your ideas below.

_____

_____

_____

_____

How Long Is a Minute?

Think about how much you can do in one minute.
Write your estimates in the Prediction column. Then time yourself.
Write the actual number in the Result column.

Prediction: In One Minute I Can   **Result**

Jump rope _____ times.	
Write the numbers 1 to _____ .	
Say the names of _____ animals.	

Balloon Clocks

Read each balloon clock. Then draw a line to connect it with the matching time.

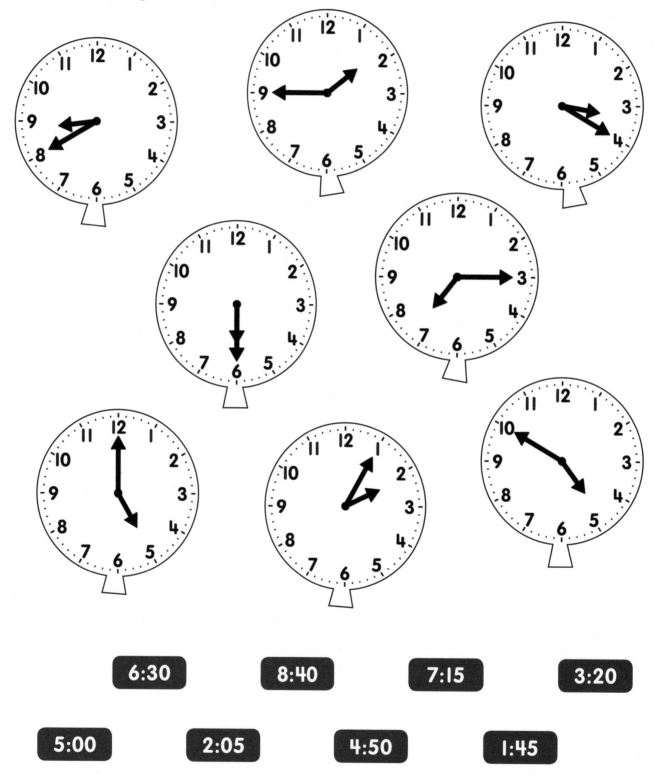

6:30   8:40   7:15   3:20

5:00   2:05   4:50   1:45

Answer Key

READING COMPREHENSION

Page 12
1. a good reader; 2. looks at the picture; 3. the title; 4. the words

Page 13
Main idea: Trucks do important work.

Page 14
Main idea: Clowns can do funny tricks.

Page 15
KATE: Names have special meanings.
Casey means brave.
George means farmer.
Sarah means princess.

Page 16

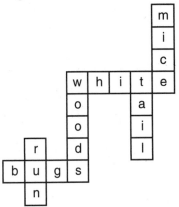

Page 17

1. in reading class; 2. camping

Page 18
Kelly packed pajamas, shirt, shorts, toothbrush, toothpaste, hairbrush, swimsuit, pillow, storybooks, sunglasses. Compound words: grandmother, suitcase, toothbrush, toothpaste, hairbrush, swimsuit, storybooks, sunglasses

Page 19
1. Texas; 2. oil; 3. President; 4. wife; 5. Jenna
His cat's name was INDIA.

Page 20
Make-believe: ketchup bottles and a watermelon bowling, a talking milk jug, dancing bananas, chicken wings that can fly all by themselves, laughing soup cans, dancing carrots

Page 21
Facts: Clouds float in the sky. Clouds are made of tiny drops of water. Fog is a cloud on the ground. (All others are make-believe.)

Page 22
Make-believe: pig, goat and sheep, horses, pizza and hamburgers, mouse and table, golden eggs, crickets (The others are real.)

Page 23
5, 1; 4, 3, 2
Tara bought pencils, scissors, glue, and crayons.

Page 24
6, 4, 2; 3, 1, 5
LEARN TO DIVE

Page 25
1. Each star should be outlined in blue and colored red inside. 2. One moon should be yellow and one orange. 3. A face should be drawn on each sun. 4. 3; 5. 2; 6. 4; 7. 3 + 2 + 4 = 9; 8. stars and moon

Page 26

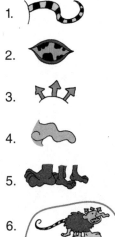

1.

2.

3.

4.

5.

6.

Page 27
The pictures that do not belong are bike, telephone, snowman, pumpkin, skates, and frog. (The other pictures should be colored.)
2. hot, cold; 3. up, down; 4. starfish; 5. yellow

Page 28

IT WAS A FLYING CARPET. No

Page 29

1. true; 2. false; 3. false; 4. true;
5. true

Page 30

Pictures should include everything
described in the sentences.

Page 31

The following should have been
added to the picture: black clouds,
lightning striking the tallest tree, the
word "Moo" in a bubble above a
cow, rain, a mud puddle by the barn
door, hay blowing out of the barn
window.

Page 32

1. penguin; 2. baby; 3. octopus;
4. ant; 5. grandmother; 6. bear;
7. firefighter

Page 33

1. head cold; 2. The children
sneezed. 3. 9; 4. She got a cold, too.

Page 34

Page 35

Bacon and eggs do not belong.

Page 36

Sandie's Shoe Store: sandals,
boots, sneakers, high heels;
Movie Town Cinema: tickets,
popcorn, big screen, candy;
Pepe's Mexican Food: tacos,
burrito, beans, peppers;
Gale's Gardening Goodies:
tulip bulbs, fertilizer, gardening
gloves, pots

Page 37

Answers will vary.

Page 38

Page 39

He knew he had to do the right
thing.

Page 40

FAST FOOD, FLOWER BED

Page 41

They are in the first grade.

Page 42

1. Juan's dad; 2. Juan's dad;
3. both; 4. Ann's dad; 5. both;
6. Ann's dad; 7. Juan's dad;
8. both; 9. Ann's dad; 10. both

Page 43

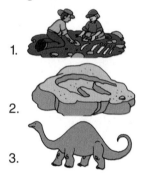

1.

2.

3.

Page 44

1. an arm like a paddle; 2. not
dangerous; 3. slap at; 4. lose;
5. hide in the ground

Page 45

1. a small city; 2. little furry animals;
3. tunnels; 4. rooms; 5. pests

Page 46
1. Sandy used lanterns at night because the cabin had no electricity. 2. Sandy and Austin bathed in a stream because the cabin had no running water. 3. Sandy felt better about missing Kendra because she talked to her on the cell phone. 4. Sandy's dad could not call his office because the cell phone was dead.

Page 47
1. The worms got tangled up when they danced. 2. They were tied in a knot so they got married.

Page 48
1. E; 2. B; 3. D; 4. F; 5. A; 6. C.

Page 49
Pictures should show a crown on Margie's arm, a shoe on her head, different colors on each fingernail, a red nose, a fork in her hair, and a purple belt around her knees.
6. the way she dresses;
7. He wears his clothes backward.

Page 50
1. happy; 2. worried; 3. silly; 4. sad; 5. scared; 6. surprised

Page 51
1. green; 2. red; 3. red; 4. yellow; 5. red; 6. yellow; 7. green

Page 52
Picture: rainbow 1. appear; 2. gold; Picture: airplane 3. high; 4. again; 5. bee

Page 53
2. Don't be greedy. Be happy with what you have. Color: dog, meat, bridge

Page 54

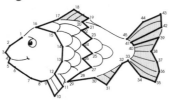

1. sharing
2. Marcus Pfister

GRAMMAR
Page 102
1. The 2. The 3. The 4. The

Page 103
1. The cat sat. 2. The dog sat.
3. I see the cat. 4. I can see.

Page 104
1. The 2. My 3. Jan 4. I 5. Ants

Page 105
1. I see Jan.
2. I go with Jan.
3. We see Dan.
4. I go with Dan and Jan.
5. school. 6. school.

Page 106
1. Dan is in the cab.
2. The cat is in the cab.
3. Mom is in the cab.
4. We see Dan and Mom.
5. van. 6. red.

Page 107
1. The cat is on the mat.
2. The rat is on the mop.
3. The rat sees the cat.
4. The rat can hop.
5. The cat and rat sit.

Page 108
1. I like to hop.
2. Pam and I like to hop.
3. I can hop to Mom.
4. Mom and I can hop.
5. Answers will vary.

Page 109
1–4. Write I on the lines.
5. Answers will vary.

Page 110
1. I sit on a mat. 2. Pam and I like cats. 3. I see the van. 4. I like jam.
5. I like to nap.

Page 111
1. Pam 2. Dan 3. The cat
4. The van
5. Jan is hot.
6. The hat is on top.
7. The man sat.

Page 112
1. Bill paints. 2. Tom likes to read.
3. Pat plants flowers.
4. Answers will vary.

Page 113
1. The cat sits on a mat. 2. Pam and Dan like jam. 3. I see Mom.
4. I like my hat. 5. Ben can hop.

Page 114
1. I 2. Pam 3. We 4. We
1. I like dots.
2. Pam likes dots.
3. We like hats.
4. We like hats with dots.

Page 115
1. I like cats. 2. I see a man.
3. We go to school

Page 116
1. I see red dots. 2. Dan is in a big van. 3. The cat is fat.
4. We like the hat. 5. Ben likes jam.

Page 117
1. ⑦ 2. ⑦ 3. ⑦ 4. ⑦
5. Answers will vary.
6. Answers will vary.

Page 118
1. Who hid the cat⑦
2. Can the cat see the rat⑦
4. Can the van go⑦
5. Can we sit in the van?
6. Can Dan nap in the van?

Page 119
1. Who hid my hat?
2. Did the hat have dots?
3. Did Jan like my hat?
4. Can you see the hat?
5. Dan has the hat?

Page 120
1. pig 2. pan 3. Pam 4. you, hill
5. The sun is hot. —— ☀
6. Sam ran and ran.
7. Is the cat fat?

Page 121
1. Al, van 2. cat, mat 3. Pat, hill
4. Dan, Jan, mop

Page 122
1. c. 2. b 3. b 4. a 5. c

Page 123
1. Ⓗill Ⓟark 2. Ⓟam 3. Ⓓon
4. Ⓕrog Ⓛake 5. Answers will vary.

Page 124
1. Pam 2. Ant Hill 3. Ron
4. Bat Lake 5. Spot 6. Hill Street

Page 125
1. Don 2. Pig Hill 3. Jam Street
4. Jan 5. Ham Lake

Page 126
1. sits 2. ran 3. hid 4. naps 5. run
6. see

Page 127
1. see 2. sits 3. mops 4. run
5. hops

Page 128
1. b 2. a 3. c 4. c 5. a

Page 129
1. big 2. fast 3. bad 4. fat
5. fat 6. little

Page 130
1. little, fast
2. hot, big
3. It is fat.
4. They are little.

Page 131
1. silly 2. bad 3. black 4. big
5. green

Page 132
1. Ⓘ see the basket◯
2. Ⓣhe cat is in the basket◯
3. Ⓗats can go in it◯
4. Ⓣhe sock can go in it◯
5. I can fill the basket.
7. We can clean.

Page 133
1. She has a mop.
2. The dog is on top.
3. Dan gets the hats.
4. Ron can clean spots.
5. Ⓟut it in the pot◯

Page 134
1. You can get it.
2. The basket is big.
3. The hat is in the basket.
4. A cat can not go in it.
5. We can fill the basket.

Page 135
1. Help! The rat is on top!
2. Get the cat!
3. This cat is bad!
4. Uh-oh! The cat is wet!
5. Oh my! Get the dog!
6. Oh! The dog runs!

Page 136
1. Run to the show!
2. Oh my, I'm very late!
3. What a great show!
4. Watch out, the floor is wet!
5. Wow, we had lots of fun!

Page 137
1. Yes! The cow can kick!
2. That cat is bad!
3. That rat runs fast!
4. Oh no! A frog is in my house!
5. The pot is hot!

Page 138
❶ Let's go
❷ I am a kid
❸ Why doesn't the clock work
❹ Do you have a hat
❺ This game is fun
❻ I play soccer
❼ What's your name
❽ The beach is great
❾ My name is Paul

!   ?   !   ?   !   ?

Page 139
1. hats 2. eggs 3. girls 4. cats
5. mugs 6. hands

Page 140
1. Jan has her mittens.
2. She will run up hills.
3. Jan runs with her dogs.
4. The dogs can jump.
5. cats 6. socks

Page 141
1. hands 2. pots 3. dogs 4. ants
5. frogs

Page 142
1. sits 2. sees 3. digs 4. naps
5. sees 6. run

Page 143
1. play 2. dance 3. talk 4. run

Page 144
1. sits 2. naps 3. hops
4. digs 5. ran

Page 145
1. We; school 2. ball 3. girl
4. friends
Person: girl Place: school
Thing: ball

Page 146
1. Run and kick
   in the (park.)
2. Kick with a (foot.)
3. Kick the (ball.)
4. The (girl) will run
   to get it.
5. Kick it to the (net.)

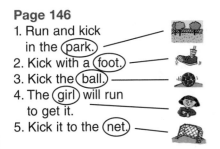

Page 147
1. park 2. girl 3. ball 4. friend
5. net

Page 148
1. The king is sad.
2. Let's bake him a cake.
3. Tell the king to come.
4. Let's eat the cake.
The king eats.

Page 149
1. This bear likes snow.
2. The water is cold.
3. The bear runs fast.
4. Two bears play.

Page 150
1. Pam will bake a cake.
2. Pam will see the king.
3. The king has a duck.
4. The duck is in the lake.
5. The king will eat cake.

Page 151
circle: What, See, Night, The, Light,
Moon, See, Many, Stars, The, Sun,
Moon
Answers will vary.

Page 152
1. look, stars 2. the, moon, shines,
night 3. we, see, planets 4. many,
moons, shine 5. night, day 6. The
Sun in the Sky 7. See the Stars!

Page 153
1. Where Is the Sun? 2. Many Cats
to See 3. Day and Night 4. How
Many Pigs? 5. The Big, Bad Wolf

Page 154
1. pot 2. pan 3. top 4. Jim
5. The pot is hot.
6. See the pan?
7. Jim is fast.

Page 155
1. Jan, van 2. van 3. van, hill
4. Dan, Jan 5. Answers will vary.

Page 156
1. pans 2. Jim 3. cat 4. rat 5. cat

Page 157
1. is 2. were 3. was 4. are 5. now
6. in the past 7. now

Page 158
1. are, now 2. is, now 3. was, past
4. is, now 5. were, past

Page 159
1. was 2. were 3. are 4. is 5. are

Page 160
1. The, Gruff 2. They, Troll 3. His,
Nosey 4. He 5. Dan and Pam like
the play. Names a person, place,
or thing. 6. They will read it to Jim.
First word in a sentence.

Page 161
1. Raul 2. Mrs. Chin 3. Sue
4. Lee Park

Page 162
1. I 2. Ron 3. Gruff 4. Troll
5. Nosey

WRITING
Page 164

The	For	That	with	know	but
here	on	When	Have	next	we
as	after	good	Make	there	see
Go	Look	Are	Could	is	why
This	who	said	in	come	them
Has	Name	Before	Her	Where	The

Page 165
1. The mouse; 2. He finds;
3. He eats; 4. Then he; 5. Oh no,;
6. The mouse

Page 166
1. We read; 2. Then we; 3. My bed;
4. My cat; 5. The sky; 6. My eyes

Page 167
1. My dog; 2. She must; 3. Maybe
she; 4. Sometimes she; 5. I think

Page 168
Check that a period has been
added to the end of each sentence.

Page 169
Check that a period has been
added to the end of each sentence.

Page 170
1. Frogs and toads lay eggs.
2. The eggs are in the water.
3. Tadpoles hatch from the eggs.
4. The tadpoles grow legs.
5. The tadpoles lose their tails.

Page 171
1. Tadpoles become frogs or toads.
2. Frogs live near water.
3. Toads live mostly on dry land.
4. Frogs have wet skin.
5. Toads have bumpy skin.

Page 172
The following sentences should be
colored red: This is a flag., The flag
has stars., The stars are white.,
The stripes are red., The stripes
are white., The flag has a blue part.,
There are 50 stars.; The rest are
not sentences and should be white.

Page 173

Page 174
Five boats are sailing.;
We have four buckets.

Page 175
A jaguar is hiding.
Some butterflies are blue.
Frogs jump in the water.
Green snakes hang from trees.
The trees grow very tall.

Page 176
The snakes on the left side of the
page should have been colored.

Page 177
1. The blue snake
2. The yellow snake
3. The green snake
4. The brown snake
5. The red snake
6. The purple snake
7. The black snake
8. The orange snake

Page 178
Sentences will vary.

Page 179
Sentences will vary.

Page 180
Sentences will vary.

Page 181
Sentences will vary.

Page 182
The bones on the right side of the
page should have been colored.

Page 183
1. is jumping.; 2. is barking.;
3. is eating.; 4. is sleeping.

Page 184
Sentences will vary.

Page 185
Answers will vary.

Page 186
Sentences will vary.

Page 187
Sentences will vary.

Page 188
Pictures will vary.

Page 189
Answers will vary.

Page 190
1. long ago; 2. yesterday;
3. in winter; 4. today; 5. in the fall;
6. last night; 7. all day; 8. at noon;
9. yesterday; 10. on Thanksgiving
Day; 11. this morning; 12. Tomorrow

Page 191
Sentences will vary.

Page 192
Answers will vary.

Page 193
Sentences will vary.

Page 194
Sentences will vary.

Page 195
Sentences will vary.

Page 196
kitten, bat, cracker, ball

Page 197
sweet, red, smooth;
bumpy, salty, crunchy;
small, squeaky, furry

Page 198
Lollipop: hard, shiny, sticky
Chick: soft, fluffy, fuzzy
Answers will vary.

Page 199
Adjectives will vary.

Page 200
Sentences will vary.

Page 201
Sentences will vary.

Page 202
Sentences will vary.

Page 203
Sentences will vary.

Page 204
Sentences will vary.

Page 205
My Space Friend; A Big Beak;
The Big Win; A Knight's Tale

Page 206
Stories will vary.

Page 207
Sentences will vary.

Page 208
Sentences and pictures will vary.

MAPS
Page 210
1. yes
2. yes
3. yes
4. no
5. swimming pool; car; lawn

Page 211
Answers should be colored
and drawn on map.

Page 212
4. truck
5. yes

Page 213
Answers should be colored
and drawn on map.

Page 215
1. far
2. near
3. above
4. right
5. left

Pages 216–217
1. yes
2. yes
3. no
4. yes
5. school
6. flower shop
7. Map 3
8. Map 1

Page 218
1. round
2. people, animals, plants
3. Drawings will vary.

Page 219
1. blue, green, orange, yellow,
purple, red
2. blue
3. smaller

Page 220
1. south
2. east

Page 221
1. east
2. north
3. west
4. south

Page 222
1. north
2. east
3. north
4. west

Page 223
1–4 Line begins at gate, runs north
to popcorn, west to Ferris wheel,
east to face painting, west to
popcorn, and north to arcade.
5. south

Page 224
1. c.   2. a.   3. d.   4. b.

Page 225
1. tree
2. airplane
3. railroad track
4. beach umbrella

Page 226
1. garden
2. road
3. house
4. stable

Page 227
1. south
2. sheep
3. west
4. Tree symbol should be drawn for forest.

Pages 228–229
1. mountain
2. plain
3. hill
4. river
5. mountain
6. hill
7. lake

Page 230
1–4 Answers should be written on picture.

Page 231
1. plain
2. east
3. west
4. Answers will vary.

Page 232
1. hill
2. campground
3. picnic table
4. river or lake
5. west

Page 233
1. Doony Park
2. snack stand
3. a fountain
4. dog run
5. playground
6. west

Page 234
1. school
2. apartment
3. store
4. house
5. Drawings will vary.

Page 235
1. school
2. Spring Street
3. Summer Street
4. west

Page 236
1. South Street
2. West Street
3. North Street
4. South Street

Page 237
1. Routes will vary.
2. East Street
4. west
5. north

Page 239
1. border
2. road
3. a river
4. south
5. west

Page 241
1. state border
2. Answers will vary.
3. Answers will vary.
4. Answers will vary.
5. south
6. west
7. Arizona
8. Indiana

Page 242
1. state capital
2. south
3. north
4. west

Page 243
1. state border
2. Ohio River
3. Wabash River
4. four
5. Lake Michigan

Page 244
1. south
2. Answers will vary.
3. west
4. east
5. Answers will vary.

Page 246
1. country border
2. Canada
3. south

Page 247
1. Atlantic Ocean
2. Pacific Ocean

Pages 248–249
2. Atlantic, Pacific, Arctic, Indian, Southern
3. Europe
4. South America
5. Indian Ocean
6. Arctic Ocean
7. Antarctica

Page 250
1. pond
2. hill
3. North Street
4. Routes will vary.
5. post office on South Street
6. north

Page 251
1. states
2. Raleigh
3. plains
4. four
5. Atlantic Ocean
6. west

Page 252
1. south
2. lake
3. border
4. symbol
5. mountain
6. route
Secret Words:
United States

SCIENCE

Page 256
2. lamb
3. tadpole
4. duck
5. fawn
6. cub
7. calf
8. piglet
9. chick
10. puppy
calf

Pages 257–261
Investigation 1: Results will vary. Your child may notice that taking small, "waddling" steps helps to keep the egg on the feet.
Investigation 2: Colors will vary. Color chosen should stand out against the habitat shown.

Page 262

Pages 263–267
Investigation 1: Signs of life will vary.
Investigation 2: Changes will vary depending on the animal chosen. Your child should consider the needs of the animal and suggest changes to accommodate it in your community park.

Page 268

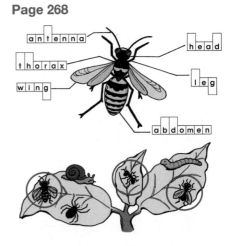
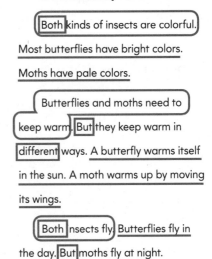

Pages 269–273
Investigation 1: The more colors of glitter your child uses, the easier it will be to see how widely the pollen has spread.
Investigation 2: Your child may decide to simply draw a flower on white paper or make a more complicated one using materials such as construction paper, pipe cleaners, and so on.

Pages 274–275
Is it a **butterfly**? Or is it a **moth**?

Both kinds of insects are colorful. Most butterflies have bright colors. Moths have pale colors.

Butterflies and moths need to keep warm. But they keep warm in different ways. A butterfly warms itself in the sun. A moth warms up by moving its wings.

Both insects fly. Butterflies fly in the day. But moths fly at night.

1. B; Sample answer: The article is about how moths and butterflies are the same and different.
2. B; Sample answer: It says in paragraph 3 that a moth warms up by moving its wings.
3. Answers will vary. Check that students' responses are different from what they underlined in the article.

Pages 276–277

Auks and hawks are birds. Like all birds, both lay eggs. Both fly and hunt.

In other ways, auks and hawks are different. Auks are black and white. Hawks come in many colors.

Auks have short legs with webbed feet. Hawks have long, strong legs. They have sharp claws.

Auks eat fish and other sea life. Hawks eat small land animals, snakes, and insects.

1. C; Sample answer: The article compares and contrasts two kinds of birds—auks and hawks.
2. B; Sample answer: The article says this in the first paragraph.
3. Sample answers: The auk is on the left. I can see its webbed feet. The hawk is on the right. I can see its sharp claws.

Page 278
Brachiosaurus, Tyrannosaurus rex, Stegosaurus, Triceratops, Trachodon; extinct

Page 279
1. C; 2. B; 3. A

Pages 280–281

Thumbs are special fingers.

All your fingers can move in and out. All can move from side to side. All can bend and wiggle. All can move in a circle. But only a thumb can touch every other fingertip. No other fingers can meet like this. Try it. Your thumbs help you grab and hold things. Can you pick up a penny without using your thumb?

1. C; Sample answer: It says in the sixth sentence that only thumbs can do this.
2. B; Sample answer: The article says that this is something thumbs help you do.
3. Sample answer: It was really hard to grab the penny without using my thumb.

Pages 282–283

Almost anything can cause a sneeze. You might breathe in some dust, cold air, or even pepper. It tickles the inside of your nose. So you need to clear it out.

Your brain gets the message. It signals some muscles to get ready to help. When they do, you suddenly feel the results. Your eyes close tight. Your mouth opens, and you sneeze: AHHH…CHOO! The tickle is gone.

1. A; Sample answer: It says this at the beginning of the second paragraph.
2. C; Sample answer: I picked C because I read the other two choices in the article.
3. Sample answer: Sneezing gets rid of a tickle inside my nose.

Page 284
1. spring; 2. winter; 3. fall;
4. summer; 5. spring; 6. winter;
7. fall; 8. summer

Pages 285–289
Investigation 1: Observations will vary depending on the season.
Investigation 2: Answers will vary depending on the season but children should be able to determine whether the days are getting shorter or longer based on the change in sunrise and sunset times over a two-week period.

Pages 290-291

A **flood** happens when water spills over. What causes a flood?

Snow melts off mountains in the spring.

It turns into water.

The water runs downhill.

It flows into rivers.

Rainstorms add more water to rivers.

Rivers can't hold all that extra water.

So they **overflow**.

The water covers everything nearby.

Floods soak fields, roads, and towns.

1. B; Sample answer: The article says that when rivers can't hold extra water, they overflow. And the first sentence says that a flood happens when water spills over.
2. C; Sample answer: The article says that melting snow and rain can cause floods. Floods happen to fields and towns.
3. Sample answer: In spring, it gets warmer and that would make snow melt and turn into water.

Page 292
2. hail; 3. tornado; 4. rain; 5. snow; 6. sunshine

Pages 293–297
Investigation 1: Blowing on the stars and triangles will work best to turn the Spin Wheel.
Investigation 2: The spinner will stay balanced when its center of gravity is at the same point as its point of support (the tip of the pencil).

Page 298

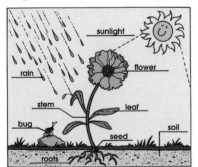

botanist

Page 299
Earth, Saturn, Mars, Mercury, Uranus, Venus, Jupiter, Neptune

Page 300
1. B 2. C 3. B

ADDITION & SUBTRACTION

Page 302

Check coloring.

Page 303
$1 + 2 = 3$, $2 + 3 = 5$, $7 + 3 = 10$;
$3 + 4 = 7$, $1 + 0 = 1$, $3 + 2 = 5$;
$1 + 1 = 2$, $4 + 4 = 8$; $1 + 3 = 4$;
The ladybug with 10 spots should be colored red. The ladybug with 1 spot should be colored blue.

Page 304
Check that the correct number of flowers have been drawn. 7: needs 3, 10: needs 5, 4: needs 1; 6: needs 2, 9: needs 5; 5: needs 3, 8: needs 4, 3: needs 2; Color the bows with the numbers 4, 6, 8, and 10 yellow. Color the bows with 3, 5, 7, and 9 purple.

Page 305
A SAXOPHONE
$6 + 2 = 8$; $5 + 1 = 6$; $4 + 4 = 8$
$3 + 6 = 9$; $3 + 0 = 3$; $3 + 4 = 7$
$2 + 2 = 4$; $2 + 1 = 3$; $1 + 1 = 2$
$0 + 1 = 1$

Page 306
$5 - 3 = 2$; $7 - 4 = 3$; $10 - 5 = 5$;
$9 - 2 = 7$; $8 - 7 = 1$; $9 - 6 = 3$;
$6 - 1 = 5$; $10 - 2 = 8$; $7 - 5 = 2$;
$5 - 1 = 4$; $8 - 2 = 6$; $8 - 0 = 8$;
$9 - 7 = 2$; $8 - 5 = 3$; $10 - 4 = 6$;
$10 - 3 = 7$; $9 - 4 = 5$; $8 - 1 = 7$;
$6 - 4 = 2$; $6 - 3 = 3$; $7 - 2 = 5$;
$9 - 0 = 9$; $10 - 1 = 9$

Page 307
2, 3, 2; 3, 2, 1

Pages 308–309
1. $9 - 4 = 5$; 2. $8 - 1 = 7$;
3. $10 - 3 = 7$; 4. $8 - 6 = 2$;
5. $7 - 2 = 5$; 6. $8 - 4 = 4$;
7. $10 - 4 = 6$; 8. $8 - 2 = 6$;
9. $9 - 6 = 3$

Page 310

Page 311

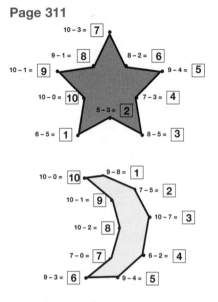

$10 - 3 = \boxed{7}$
$9 - 1 = \boxed{8}$ $8 - 2 = \boxed{6}$
$10 - 1 = \boxed{9}$ $9 - 4 = \boxed{5}$
$10 - 0 = \boxed{10}$ $7 - 3 = \boxed{4}$
$5 - 3 = \boxed{2}$
$6 - 5 = \boxed{1}$ $8 - 5 = \boxed{3}$

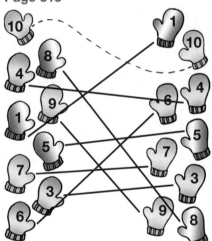

$10 - 0 = \boxed{10}$ $9 - 8 = \boxed{1}$
$7 - 5 = \boxed{2}$
$10 - 1 = \boxed{9}$
$10 - 7 = \boxed{3}$
$10 - 2 = \boxed{8}$
$7 - 0 = \boxed{7}$ $6 - 2 = \boxed{4}$
$9 - 3 = \boxed{6}$ $9 - 4 = \boxed{5}$

Page 312

4, 3, 2; 10, 1, 7; 6, 8, 5;
The rabbit moved right to add.
The rabbit moved left to subtract.

Page 313

Page 314

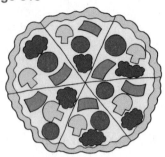

IT'S OUT OF THIS WORLD!

Page 315

A. $6 + 2 = 8$; B. $3 + 1 = 4$;
C. $6 - 4 = 2$

Page 316

A. $6 + 4 = 10$; B. $10 - 5 = 5$;
C. $9 - 2 = 7$; D. $4 + 6 = 10$;
E. $7 + 2 = 9$; F. $2 + 3 = 5$;
G. $5 + 3 = 8$; H. $6 + 4 = 10$;
I. $8 - 7 = 1$; J. $10 - 3 = 7$

Page 317

A. $7 + 3 = 10$; B. $7 - 4 = 3$;
C. $10 - 6 = 4$; D. $8 - 2 = 6$;
E. $5 + 4 = 9$

Page 318

Check coloring.
11 ways; $0 + 10 = 10$, $1 + 9 = 10$,
$2 + 8 = 10$, $3 + 7 = 10$, $4 + 6 = 10$,
$5 + 5 = 10$, $6 + 4 = 10$, $7 + 3 = 10$,
$8 + 2 = 10$, $9 + 1 = 10$, $0 + 10 = 10$

Page 319

7 leaps

Page 320

$8 + 7 = 15$; $3 + 7 = 10$; $8 + 6 = 14$;
$9 + 9 = 18$; $1 + 1 = 2$; $5 + 2 = 7$;
$3 + 2 = 5$; $9 + 2 = 11$; $4 + 2 = 6$;
$1 + 4 = 5$; $2 + 2 = 4$; $7 + 4 = 11$;
$5 + 8 = 13$; $6 + 2 = 8$; $7 + 7 = 14$;
$5 + 5 = 10$; $4 + 7 = 11$; $3 + 3 = 6$;
$1 + 7 = 8$; $3 + 8 = 11$; $5 + 0 = 5$;
$9 + 6 = 15$; $5 + 3 = 8$; $2 + 5 = 7$;
$0 + 2 = 2$; $3 + 1 = 4$; $9 + 7 = 16$;
$7 + 5 = 12$; $6 + 1 = 7$; $9 + 8 = 17$;
$1 + 5 = 6$; $6 + 6 = 12$
Elephant

Page 321

Beans talk.

$4 + 2 = 6$; $7 + 7 = 14$; $9 + 5 = 14$
$10 + 4 = 14$; $4 + 8 = 12$; $6 + 8 = 14$
$11 + 3 = 14$; $14 + 0 = 14$; $7 + 2 = 9$
$13 + 1 = 14$; $5 + 8 = 13$; $12 + 2 = 14$
$7 + 4 = 11$; $5 + 9 = 14$

Page 322

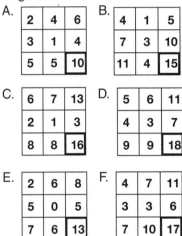

A.

2	4	6
3	1	4
5	5	10

B.

4	1	5
7	3	10
11	4	15

C.

6	7	13
2	1	3
8	8	16

D.

5	6	11
4	3	7
9	9	18

E.

2	6	8
5	0	5
7	6	13

F.

4	7	11
3	3	6
7	10	17

Page 323

8, 8; 4, 4; 6, 6; 8, 8; 1, 1; 3, 3; 9, 9;
2, 2; 5, 5; 7, 7; even

Page 324

$7 + 7 = 14$, $5 + 5 = 10$, $8 + 8 = 16$,
$6 + 6 = 12$; $9 + 9 = 18$, $3 + 3 = 6$,
$2 + 2 = 4$; $4 + 4 = 8$

Page 325

A. 4; B. 6; C. 10; D. 9; E. 7; F. 2;
G. 5; H. 8; I. 3; J. 1; K. $5 - 2 = 3$;
L. $9 - 3 = 6$; M. $7 - 5 = 2$;
N. $8 - 1 = 7$; O. $12 - 6 = 6$;
P. $16 - 8 = 8$; Q. $14 - 5 = 9$

Page 326

four, five; seven, eleven; nine, six;
ten, three; eight, two

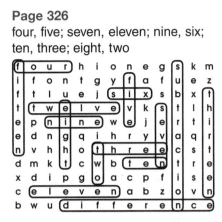

Page 327

$7 + 2 = 9 - 4 = 5 - 3 = 2 + 9 = 11 +$
$5 = 16 - 8 = 8 + 4 = 12 + 6 = 18 - 9$
$= 9 + 1 = 10 + 4 = 14 - 8 = 6 + 2 =$
$8 + 3 = 11 - 3 = 8$;
$12 - 3 = 9 - 6 = 3 + 2 = 5 + 9 = 14$
$- 6 = 8 + 7 = 15 - 6 = 9 + 3 = 12 -$
$2 = 10 + 7 = 17 + 1 = 18 - 11 = 7 -$
$5 = 2 + 13 = 15 - 7 = 8 + 3 = 11$;
Color the bottom car blue.

Page 328

3 peanuts

Page 329

3, 3; 7, 7; 9, 9; 5, 5; 8, 8

Page 330

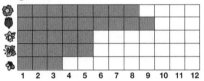

A. First flower should be circled.;
B. $8 + 9 = 17$; C. $5 - 5 = 0$;
D. $5 + 3 = 8$; E. $5 - 3 = 2$;
F. $9 + 5 = 14$

Page 331

A. 13, 12, 13, 13; B. 12, 11, 11, 11;
C. 17, 15, 15, 17; D. 14, 14, 14, 16
Check coloring.

Page 332

-1; 12, 11, 10, 9, 8, 7
$+2$; 2, 4, 6, 8, 10, 12
$+3$; 3, 6, 9, 12, 15, 18
-2; 13, 11, 9, 7, 5, 3

Page 333

2, 4, 2; 3, 5, 4; 6, 4, 10;
Answers will vary.

Page 334

5; 3 + 2 + 5 = 10; 4 + 5 + 7 = 16; 6;
7 + 2 = 9; 6 − 2 = 4; 7 + 4 + 5 + 3 +
2 = 21; 1 + 7 + 6 + 3 + 2 = 19

Page 335

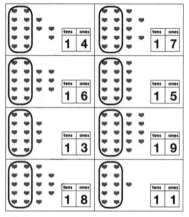

Page 336

Check coloring; 14 days

Page 337

17	36	84		
78	29	59	14	48
88	24	35	66	98
18	43	77	38	88
78	65	56	46	26
	99	57	87	

Page 338

93 + 6 = 99, 82 + 4 = 86, 14 + 5 =
19, 21 + 7 = 28, 53 + 6 = 59;
45 + 4 = 49, 73 + 3 = 76, 36 + 3 =
39, 61 + 5 = 66, 32 + 7 = 39;
4 + 7 + 5 + 3 + 6 = 25

Page 339

Page 340

Check coloring.

Page 341

A. 39 − 7 = 32; B. 54 − 1 = 53;
C. 87 − 6 = 81; D. 73 − 3 = 70;
E. 25 − 4 = 21; F. 42 − 2 = 40;
G. 98 − 7 = 91; H. 66 − 5 = 61;
4, 7, 5

Page 342

42, 90, 76, 32, 82, 63, 81; 50, 35,
21, 21, 41, 90, 53; 30, 80, 20, 70,
60, 65, 74; The box with 53 should
be colored yellow. The box with 32
should be colored orange. The box
with 74 should be colored red.

Page 343

Check coloring.

Page 344

AT
12 + 13 = 25; 24 + 34 = 58;
22 + 21 = 43; 77 + 22 = 99;
35 + 43 = 78; 52 + 12 = 64;
40 + 52 = 92; 11 + 31 = 42;
30 + 39 = 69; 46 + 52 = 98;
15 + 12 = 27; 10 + 71 = 81;
63 + 11 = 74; 13 + 80 = 93;
36 + 32 = 68; 30 + 10 = 40;
11 + 11 = 22; 15 + 4 = 19;
20 + 21 = 41; 15 + 11 = 26;
22 + 33 = 55; 14 + 14 = 28;
13 + 16 = 29; 10 + 20 = 30;
14 + 25 = 39; 11 + 20 = 31;
15 + 21 = 36; 20 + 31 = 51;
36 + 52 = 88; 21 + 32 = 53;
10 + 50 = 60; 44 + 41 = 85;
24 + 43 = 67; 31 + 21 = 52;
13 + 82 = 95

Page 345

32 + 24 = 56; 16 + 40 = 56;
54 + 14 = 68; 77 + 12 = 89;
34 + 34 = 68; 53 + 36 = 89;
26 + 63 = 89; 23 + 45 = 68;
35 + 62 = 97; 38 + 30 = 68;
22 + 67 = 89; 47 + 42 = 89

Page 346

HE WAS A CHICKEN.
13 + 11 = 24; 26 + 33 = 59;
16 + 31 = 47; 10 + 12 = 22;
64 + 24 = 88; 20 + 15 = 35;
71 + 12 = 83; 25 + 21 = 46;
51 + 10 = 61; 22 + 16 = 38;
22 + 10 = 32; 14 + 14 = 28;
20 + 10 = 30; 25 + 31 = 56;
21 + 3 = 24; 42 + 30 = 72;
13 + 43 = 56; 54 + 15 = 69;
21 + 61 = 82; 61 + 33 = 94;
10 + 30 = 40; 20 + 30 = 50;
16 + 32 = 48; 71 + 23 = 94;
70 + 20 = 90

Page 347

A BAT
5 − 2 = 3; 7 − 7 = 0; 18 − 9 = 9;
17 − 3 = 14; 15 − 4 = 11;
18 − 4 = 14; 12 − 3 = 9;
11 − 9 = 2; 16 − 9 = 7; 7 − 4 = 3;
10 − 8 = 2; 15 − 7 = 8; 9 − 2 = 7;
13 − 2 = 11; 12 − 2 = 10;
15 − 2 = 13; 9 − 6 = 3; 6 − 6 = 0;
9 − 7 = 2; 15 − 9 = 6; 16 − 8 = 8;
9 − 5 = 4; 9 − 1 = 8

Page 348

77 − 30 = 47; 76 − 62 = 14;
59 − 12 = 47; 85 − 52 = 33;
98 − 84 = 14; 87 − 40 = 47;
98 − 35 = 63; 58 − 11 = 47;
88 − 62 = 26; 77 − 14 = 63;
69 − 22 = 47; 38 − 12 = 26;
75 − 12 = 63; 97 − 71 = 26;
97 − 50 = 47; 98 − 51 = 47;
43 − 10 = 33; 87 − 73 = 14;
78 − 31 = 47; 97 − 64 = 33;
99 − 52 = 47

Page 349

1. 7 − 1 = 6; 2. 9 − 2 = 7;
3. 3 − 2 = 1; 4. 8 − 4 = 4,
5. 5 − 5 = 0; 6. 6 − 1 = 5;
7. 8 − 2 = 6
The phone number is 671-4056.

Page 350

27, 74, 41, 65; 27, 70, 42, 53;
15, 23, 11, 33; 20, 2, 15, 31; 22

Page 351

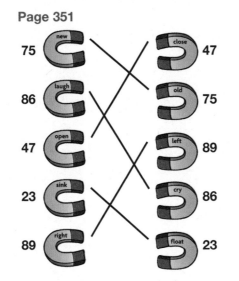

Answers will vary.

Page 352

34 + 13 = 47, 21 + 52 = 73, 47 + 10
= 57; 75 − 34 = 41, 62 − 21 = 41,
47 − 13 = 34

Page 353

A. Sunday; B. 89;
C. Monday; D. 24; E. 79; F. 22;
Sunday, Tuesday, Saturday

Page 354

34, 85, 26, 57; star; 71, 88, 42, 76,
85; light; 76, 63, 26, 85; heat; 71,
88, 13, 63; life

Page 355

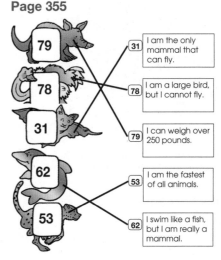

Page 356

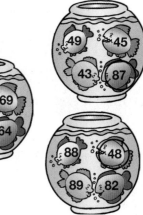

Answers will vary.

MATH

Page 358

Page 359
Answers will vary, but check to make sure that the correct numbers have been supplied for each category.

Page 360
Check to make sure that the lines are drawn from five different frogs to the lily pads.
No; 2 frogs need lily pads

Page 361
1. Answers will vary.
2. Numbers will be colored in using an AB pattern of red and blue.

Page 362
Possible groups
Balls: soccer ball, basketball, rubber ball
Winter clothes: scarf, hat, boots
Art supplies: paint, paintbrush, crayon

Page 363

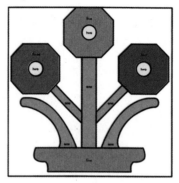

Page 364
Yield sign: triangle, 3
Caution sign: diamond, 4
Speed-limit sign: rectangle, 4
Stop sign: octagon, 8

Page 365
Left birdhouse: cube, octagon, hexagon, rectangle, square, rectangle solid
Right birdhouse: cylinder, triangle, circle, rectangle

Page 366
Color the first butterfly, the second heart, the lightbulb, and the snowflake; drawings should show the other halves.

Page 367
1. 32, 42, 52, 62, 72, 82, 92
2. 70, 60, 50, 40, 30, 20, 10
3. 67, 57, 47, 37, 27, 17, 7
4. 44, 55, 66, 77, 88, 99

Page 368
A salamander

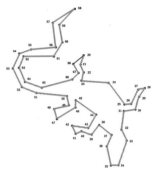

Page 369
Estimates will vary. 2, 4, 6, 8, 10, 12, 14, 16, 18, 20, 5, 10, 15, 20
Extra: No. Snowflakes would melt before you could count them.

Page 370

1	2	3	4	5	6	7	8	9	10
11	12	13	14	15	16	17	18	19	20
21	22	23	24	25	26	27	28	29	30
31	32	33	34	35	36	37	38	39	40
41	42	43	44	45	46	47	48	49	50
51	52	53	54	55	56	57	58	59	60
61	62	63	64	65	66	67	68	69	70
71	72	73	74	75	76	77	78	79	80
81	82	83	84	85	86	87	88	89	90
91	92	93	94	95	96	97	98	99	100

Answers will vary.

Page 371
Check drawings.
3 + 2 = 5; 4 + 1 = 5
5 + 3 = 8; 2 + 6 = 8
2 + 4 = 6; 3 + 3 = 6

Page 372

4 + 4 = 8
5 + 5 = 10
6 + 6 = 12
7 + 7 = 14
8 + 8 = 16
Extra: 6, 8, 10, 12, 14, 16
Pattern: Count by 2s, even numbers, doubling

Page 373

Patterns and equations will vary.

Page 374

5; Answers will vary.

Page 375

Answers will vary.

Page 376

Answers will vary.

Page 377

15; 8

Page 378

Alex's coins: 25¢ + 25¢ + 10¢ = 60¢
Billy's coins: 10¢ + 10¢ + 10¢ +
10¢ + 10¢ + 5¢ + 5¢ + 1¢ + 1¢ + 1¢
= 63¢
63¢ > 60¢ Billy has more money.

Page 379

1¢: 10 coins for 10¢
5¢: 4 coins for 20¢
10¢: 2 coins for 20¢
25¢: 2 coins for 50¢

Page 380

Answers will vary.

Page 381

3 1/2 inches, 2 inches,
1 1/2 inches, 3 inches
Patty, Peter, Petunia, Paul

Page 382

pencil: 2
lunchbox: 1
crayon: 2
notebook: 1

Page 383

1 gallon = 4 quarts
1 quart = 2 pints
1 pint = 2 cups
1 cup = 12 tablespoons
1 tablespoon = 3 teaspoons

Page 384

1 + 2 + 1 + 2 = 6 inches
2 + 3 + 2 + 3 = 10 inches
2 + 5 + 2 + 5 = 14 inches

Page 385

book height: 2 centimeters
book width: 3 centimeters
straw: 6 centimeters
marker: 4 centimeters
5 cubes: 4 centimeters
10 cubes: 8 centimeters
shoe: 5 centimeters
hand: 3 centimeters

Page 386

Answers will vary. Check graph
to make sure that it corresponds
to the boxes checked.
chicken: see, hear, smell, touch
sun: see
lemonade: see, touch, taste
flowers: see, smell, touch
drums: see, hear, touch

Page 387

Answers will vary.

Page 388

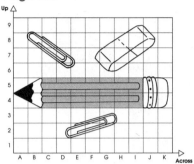

Page 389

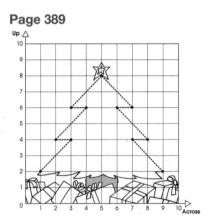

Page 390

Sunny days: 12
Cloudy days: 8
Rainy days: 5
Snowy days: 6

Page 391

Color shapes 1, 2, 5, 6, 7, and 8.

Page 392

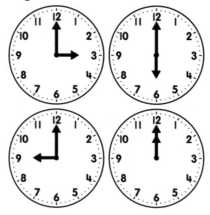

Page 393

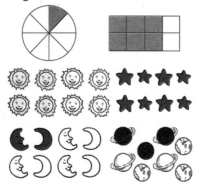

Page 394

Page 395

Page 396

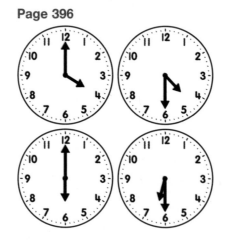

Page 397
Answers will vary.

Page 398

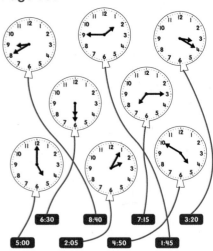